Summary Bu

Health | Rea

Publishing: Includes Summary

of A Simplified Life &

Summary of Allen Carr's Easy

Way to Stop Smoking

ABBEY BEATHAN

Legal & Disclaimer

directly or indirectly, of any advice or information presented, whether for breach of contract, tort, negligence, personal injury, criminal intent, or under any other cause of action.

You agree to accept all risks of using the information presented inside this book. You need to consult a professional medical practitioner in order to ensure you are both able and healthy enough to participate in this program.

Table of Contents

These warm, enjoyable, and fun occasions form the good
stuff of life. They are the moments which forge your
marriage, shape your children, and strengthen your
friendships. 7. Simplified Technology - Creating Healthy
Tech Boundaries and Corralling Gadgets............................44

The Book at a Glance

What can you expect from reading this book?

Chapter 1 is about how you can make life seem less overwhelming by simplifying your space. It gives you tips on how to get rid of excessive physical stuff, a foundational step that gives you immediate and rewarding transformational results.

Chapter 2 guides you through the steps necessary to establish a wardrobe and beauty routine that is easy, simple, and convenient. It teaches you how to figure out a signature style that works for you – a simple and practical style with which you will be happy and comfortable.

Chapter 3 helps you with tips on how to simplify meals. It suggests ways to help you come up with nourishing, easy-to-prepare meals so you can turn dinnertime from a rushed and frantic experience into an enjoyable and relaxing time with your family.

Chapter 4 tells you how to simplify your schedule. It points out how important it is to put in margins. Margins allow you to focus on the important instead of rushing through so many activities – most of which may not even contribute to making your life more abundant in joy and meaning.

Chapter 5 talks about the importance of staying on top of your finances. It explores the simple steps you can take in order to reduce financial anxiety and gain financial freedom. It points out how applying basic, easy-to-follow- rules can help you steer your way effectively through financial problems and emerge more confident, happier, and less anxious about the financial aspect of your life.

Chapter 6 deals with simplified hospitality – the acts of loving service you can show your family, friends, and loved ones to make them feel loved and appreciated. It points out that such acts do not have to be elaborate or highly detailed. You can use the resources already available to you to show your affection in ways that are simple yet meaningful.

Chapter 7 points out how lives have dramatically changed because of technology. Technology has its definite advantages. However, it is in your family's best interest if you create certain limitations in the use of modern-day gadgets. You have to establish family rules to protect the people you love, particularly your young children from the perils of a world that is constantly plugged-in and connected.

Chapter 8 underscores the fact that you need to take care of yourself if you want to serve others well. It gives you tips on how to replenish your well so that it does not run dry and keep you from joyfully tending your love obligations.

Chapter 9 zeroes in on how you can assume your role as a loving mother who can effectively raise her children into loving, joyful, and happy adults. It offers techniques which you can apply so that you are able to raise your family with order, style, structure and a lot of joy.

Chapter 10 points out that you have to make time and space to practice your faith. It highlights the importance of putting God first. It points out how praying with trust and confidence can infuse your life with joy and vitality.

E-book Instructions

You will maximize the use of this e-book if you utilize your device's note-taking and highlighting functions. It helps to document your thoughts and responses when you read parts that resonate with you.

Introduction

Life can often seem overwhelming. However, you can do something to make it less so. You can manage certain areas in your life so that you enjoy moments of peace, comfort, and satisfaction. You can simplify your life by simply putting in a little intention, persistence, and effort.

You have to consciously carve out space – physical and mental -- so you can pay attention and savor what really matters. This book seeks to provide tactical tools which you may find useful for intentional living. The techniques will help you in your effort to eliminate clutter, build functional routines into daily life, and formulate organizational strategies for your family.

The author grew up with a mother who tried to make life simple and pleasant. Now she is trying to do the same for her own family – and now shares her own strategies for success.

Homemaking should center on freeing up space and time so that you have more resources to demonstrate your love your family, loved ones, and friends.

The book presents essential techniques for simplifying 10 principal areas of life. These techniques focus on eliminating distractions, setting up systems and tools, and creating practical and flexible routines that actually work

The goal is to make each aspect of life work in harmony, instead of competing for your time and attention.

The book provides tips and tricks for simplified living. It includes practical systems that will help you make life simpler for your busy family. These techniques aim to help you shape a life that is sweet, uncomplicated, and rich – very much like the life that the author continues to build with her own family.

You, too, can make small and big changes in the way you live in order to attain simple bliss. Life has to be made simple in order to be savored. You cannot tune in to simple joys if your life is constantly on over-drive.

To simplify life is to pare it down to the essential parts that really matter. Doing so allows you to do the things that need to be done – and gives you the luxury to relax, enjoy life with your loved ones, and relish life with your whole mind, heart, and spirit.

1. Simplified Space - Creating a Decluttered, Meaningful Home

You can start your journey towards intentional living by simplifying your space. This is foundational – and results in immediate, powerful, and rewarding transformations. When you simplify your space, you give your home the resources to soothe, inspire, and foster joy and contentment.

Define your Space

When you put love and order into your home, you are "making a home." Homemaking is the art and science of creating and managing a home so that it becomes a pleasing place to live in. This involves crafting, ordering, and managing your home so that it is able to foster love, life, and joyful memories.

Clutter, the principal enemy of simplicity, is one obstacle you have to conquer. Clutter distracts. It draws your attention from what matters. It distracts you from the things you need to attend to. It makes it difficult for you to rest and relax.

Do your bookshelves overflow with knickknacks and magazines? Is there several days' worth of unopened mail on your mantelpiece? Are there unwashed dishes on the sink and cooking utensils on your kitchen counter?

When you walk through the door and find all these things in your home, you tend to feel overwhelmed. Your space does that to you even before you have even lay down your purse.

Make a Personal Inventory

What is it about your life that seems less than simple?

What kind of home do you want for your family?

What ambiance, aesthetic, or elements in home design are you particularly drawn to?

Why do you think it essential to put heart and effort into making your dwelling place a "home" for your family?

Do a Ruthless Clean-out

Every single scrap of clutter keeps you from having your dream home.

The author says that when she realized the extent of distraction that the things in her home were causing her, she resolved to do a ruthless clean-out. The effect was simply amazing. Reducing clutter helped the author achieve simplicity, serenity, and a great sense of lightness.

It is not enough to employ fancy organizational systems or

costly organizers. You have to get rid of excess. Your home should hold only what is essential and useful, as well as a few well-chosen cherished treasures. When you are able to get rid of excess, you have fewer things to clean or pick up, less chores to do, and less visual clutter to distract you. You will breath more easily and realize how much physical, emotional, and mental effort it takes to maintain a lot of things – most of which you actually can do without.

Simplifying your space takes time. Prepare for a marathon, not for a dash or sprint.

Make a list of all the spaces in your home. Include every bedroom, bathroom, closet, guest room, living room, kitchen, laundry room, pantry, storage, office, hall, attic, and every little cranny.

Work with one room at a time. Start with the one which seems most overwhelming.

Assign one room as your "get-these-things-out-of-this-home" space. Put all the things you weed out in this room – ready to donate or throw out.

Be organized about clearing things out. If you are working on a drawer, take everything out of that drawer. Take each thing and carefully consider that. Do you absolutely need it? Do you totally love it? Do you have something similar to it? When was the last time you used it?

Be strict with yourself. Keep only an item if it is extremely necessary or if it is an heirloom you cannot absolutely part with. Keep in mind that you cannot keep all items that seem special to you right now otherwise your home will burst with your kids' projects, stuffed animals, and the dead flowers your kids have handed you at one time or another.

Get rid of multiples and items you have outgrown. Eliminate everything that is unnecessary or broken. Remove things which you plan to use "one of these days."

It is not your goal to make your home sparse or bare. Your goal is to get rid of distractions so you can focus on, enjoy, and treasure the things that really matter.

Sort and Organize your Things

Keep similar items together. This is essential to the decluttering process. When your things are organized, you know exactly where to look for them when you need them.

If you decide to keep a few really special heirlooms, keep them in a couple of keepsake boxes. Keep cherished art projects, mementos, and photographs in these boxes. When you add new things to these boxes, you may have to remove some things.

Keep in mind that you want to simplify and keep things out of sight as much as possible. Visual clutter takes its toll. It vies for your attention. It makes you feel overwhelmed, tired, and uninspired. Think of an empty or open space as breathing room – for both your mind and your home. Open spaces allow you to focus on filling your home with tradition, love, and creativity.

Be practical and sensible.

Once you have pared down your things, keep bins and boxes in strategic places. Install big hooks near your front door. Designate space for your kids' backpacks, your go-to purse, and your spouse's briefcase to make the morning rush more manageable.

Do not give in to the trend of being over-organized – of labeling every single container or stacking things in neat little rows. Apply what works best for your family and your lifestyle.

Make your way through every room. Donate the things you have weeded out to the Salvation Army or some similar organization.

After you have simplified your space, you will feel a deep

sense of achievement and freedom. Streamlining and getting rid of clutter allows you to make your home a place of genuine relaxations, rest, and refuge.

2. Simplified Style - Establishing a Simple Wardrobe and Beauty Routine

Most people feel rushed in the morning. You can make life simpler by adapting a simplified style that incorporates a simple beauty and wardrobe routine.

Simplifying Your Wardrobe

You do not want a closet that is full of clothes that do not fit anymore or those that demand a lot of ironing and maintenance or are too worn or outmoded. If you have fewer (and better) options, you are faced with simpler decisions. You are also much more likely to make choices that make you happy.

Opt to maintain a "capsule wardrobe." The term was originally used to refer to a manageable (twelve items or less) wardrobe of high-quality basic pieces that you could mix and match to craft an enduring signature style.

Today's capsule wardrobe is usually made up of about forty pieces which you can accessorize based on seasons with a handful of trendy items. The purpose of the wardrobe is to provide you with everything you need without having any item that is unnecessary.

Declutter Your Closet

When you create your personal capsule wardrobe, you have to ruthlessly and intentionally declutter your closet. Your goal is to achieve a simple space that results in a clear mind.

Take everything out of your closet. Review each item according to these criteria:

- Does it fit?

- Is it of good quality?

- Is it a favorite?

Set aside every item that fails to meet these criteria. Sell or donate these items.

Keep out-of-season "keepers' out of sight by putting them in storage bags or boxes.

Create a Simple Signature Style

After the weeding out process, look at the items you have decided to keep. Ask yourself how you want to feel when wearing your clothes. What do the items you have chosen reflect about your signature style?

Knowing your signature style simplifies the process of

putting an outfit together. It makes you feel your best. It makes you feel confident and comfortable in your clothes.

A signature style simplifies shopping. It makes it easier for you to decide what to wear.

When you go shopping, remember that you do not need to have the trendiest item. You do not have to buy an item simply because it is on sale. Look for quality. Consider an item carefully before deciding to buy it. Shop mindfully.

Go through this same process when you go through your shoes, jewelry, and other accessories. Keep only what you really use and love. Get rid of everything else. If there is a piece of jewelry that you want to hand down to a daughter later on, set it aside in a box until it is time to give it away.

Beauty Basics

Keep your make-up routine basic. Keep it simple and consistent.

Keep Only Makeup Items that are Essential

Choose a handful of high-quality, long-lasting, and timeless products that go with your signature style. Get rid of any makeup item that tends to sabotage a simplified beauty routine.

Toss all makeup that is past its expiration date. When you open an item, mark the date on the bottle or case. Toss the following after a certain time has passed:

- Mascara: 3-6 months
- Eyeliner: 6 months-1 year
- Foundation in pot: 6 months
- Foundation in pump bottle: 1-2 years
- Powder cosmetics like eye shadow or blush: 1-2 years
- Nail polish: 1-2 years
- Lipstick: 2 years
- Perfume: 8 to10 years

Make sure that your makeup bag has only the necessities. You will not waste time going through the bag to find what you need and use on a day-to-day basis. (You can keep a few additional selections of lipstick for formal events).

Master the Proper Techniques for Makeup Application

If you know exactly how to apply your makeup, you can put it on much more quickly. You also look more polished and avoid waste.

Maintain the same day-to-day look. If you are going out on a special date or attending a formal occasion, you can tweak your makeup a little to go with the special occasion.

Otherwise, be consistent.

Create a Signature Hair Style

Look for a hairstyle that fits you and is comfortable and low-maintenance.

When you have established a simple wardrobe and a basic beauty routine, preparing yourself for the day ahead becomes faster, easier, and less complicated.

3. Simplified Meals - Taking the Stress Out of Meal Planning

One big cause of stress at home is food. Deciding what to buy and prepare and getting food on the table can be a frustrating and overwhelming task.

Dinnertime should be an occasion for nourishing the body, connecting with the family, and resting and relaxing after a hard day at work or school. It should be a time to be enjoyed and savored.

Most of the time, however, dinnertime is rushed, frantic, and chaotic. It is a rowdy way to cap a busy day, rather than a revered respite from disorder and busyness.

Simplifying Meals

How can you simplify meals so that it becomes a process you can enjoy and luxuriate in rather than be stressed by?

Declutter

The first step is to declutter.

You have to clean out your spice rack, pantry, refrigerator, and other food spaces. You have to tackle kitchen drawers and cabinets that hold your dishes, cutlery, cooking utensils, and kitchen equipment. You have to free up space so you can craft meaningful and joyful mealtimes with the people you love.

The pantry is one of the more problematical spaces in the kitchen.

Clear all the shelves.

Imagine the "zones" which will work best for you. Organizing things into distinct zones makes it easier and faster to look for the things that you need. Work in the kitchen becomes simpler and more efficient.

Consider the products that you make use of. If you have small kids, store cereal boxes and packaged snacks at kids' eye level. Opt to keep dry food supplies – dry food, as well as spices, aluminum foil, etc., in the pantry rather than in the kitchen.

Put back the things you decide to use. Discard anything that is past its expiration date. Throw away items which you are pretty sure you will not use prior to expiry date.

Do the same thing with the things in your refrigerator.

Make Things Simple

Using a lot of labeled containers and bins may be counterproductive and expensive. They may just overcomplicate your fridge and pantry.

For example, removing beans or oatmeal from their original packaging and putting them in luxurious glass containers or acrylic boxes may be too much work. And you lose the expiry date as well.

Do not keep things that you hardly use. Toss or give them away.

Your objective is to keep your options at a minimum. You will find joy in maintaining only one set of high-quality dinner plates, one each of must-have gadgets (who needs two vegetable peelers?) and 3 to 5 (instead of 20) of the cookbooks that you refer to most often. If you need to have extra staples, keep them to a minimum to save kitchen space and decision time.

Establish a Simple Meal Planning Routine

If you plan meals as a matter of habit, the task becomes easier and less overwhelming.

Choose a particular day for meal planning and grocery

shopping.

Write down the meals you intend to prepare for every day of the week. You can plan for simple and easy-to-make breakfasts and lunches. Incorporate food that your family loves. For example, the author shares that her family enjoys having either bagels with cream cheese or parfaits made of granola and Greek yogurt for breakfast. She makes either pasta salad or turkey sandwiches for lunch.

For dinner, she usually includes three to four meals, a left-over meal day, a Friday pizza party (a tradition her family adores), and one dinner out. For Sunday, when she usually has more time to prepare, she may opt to prepare a fancier meal.

She keeps a list of tried-and-tested, healthy, easy-to-prepare, and well-loved family recipes that she chooses from. Sometimes, she tries a new recipe. Most of the time, she sticks to her family's favorites and prepares them in rotation.

After planning out the weekly menu, she draws up her grocery list. She adds these items to a list of fresh staples that she buys every single week – fruit, bread, cheese, milk, deli turkey, and the like.

She organizes her list (dry items which are found on the aisles of the store and fresh, found in the outer perimeter) to make her trip to the supermarket quick and easy.

For the author, meal planning takes the stress out of preparing dinner. In the morning, she simply consults her planner and lays out the food that needs to be thawed or chopped. Cooking the meal in the evening is made easy and makes for a more relaxed and joyful family time.

The author says that she may not remember the fancy meals her mom prepared for them when she was a child but she certainly remembers the focused time that her mom spent with them. She hopes that her kids will also be able to look back on their childhood with the same fondness.

Make Dinnertime Special

There are several simple ways to make dinnertime special for your family.

If it works for you, you can opt to use your best dishes, candles, and real napkins to make dinner feel really special, even when you are just having pizza.

Start the meal by saying a blessing together.

Enjoy the meal as a time to nourish your body, as well as a time to bond with each member of the family. Encourage conversation. Listen attentively to each other. Encourage each member to share and talk about what he considers the most memorable parts of his day.

4. Simplified Schedule - Maintaining a Calendar with Margin

A planner helps you "fix" a busy life. It helps you plan and manage your schedules.

However, no matter how good a planner is, it will not fix your life. Time and emotional and brain space are limited. Every commitment chips away at these resources. If you crave simplicity and have days that are intentional, you have to declutter your calendar. You have to eliminate the excess and retain just the essentials.

Make Margins

If you want to have a rich and rewarding life, you have to simplify your schedule.

Decide on Priorities

You have to consciously define the way you want to live your life. You have to declare, without any apology, what matters to you the most. When you plan your days, you have to honor these priorities. You have to get rid of the distractions that pull your mind and heart away from them. You have to say no to some things so that you give yourself, as well as your calendar, the breathing room that is needed.

It is good to apply the brakes, sit down to identify potential problem areas, and create the necessary changes.

Be Fully Present

It is not just the clear-cut, obvious commitments that muddle your schedules. When your mental space is overcrowded, your focus is compromised. When you spend time with your kids but you are actually worrying about your work, you fail to give your heart to the kids you are physically spending time with. You are not 100% present.

Simplify your schedule so that you can focus and be fully present. Create margins in your schedule so that you do not get overwhelmed. When you keep a tight schedule, your health and relationships suffer. You become overwhelmed. You are likely to crash and burn.

Review what "Success" Means to You and Your Family

It is good to establish your definition of a "successful" life. Is it a flourishing career? Is it a joyful family? How do you address competing priorities?

The author shares that she used to have a jam-packed schedule. She had an over-busy life. She relentlessly pursued one achievement after another and pushed herself hard.

She and her husband decided to sit down to look at what they really thought comprised "success" for their family. They decided it was about spending more time with their family and less on chasing extremely high financial goals. They swore to make a conscious effort to slow down and cherish the inevitably chaotic season of life with three kids below the age of six. They decided that their health, marriage, and relationship with their kids were of utmost importance to them. Based on these realizations, they made major changes at home and at work.

The author says that she made space in her life for being a room mom for her son's class. She began to accept random play dates. She created simple and fun stay-at-home family traditions. She turned down some work opportunities, not necessarily because they conflicted with her personal schedules, but because she wanted breathing space to inspire her mind and heart.

She weaned herself from her always-busy ways. She trained herself to work more carefully and mindfully. She found genuine joy in working from home and playing on the floor with her kids. She found inspiration in nurturing herself and her small family.

Juggling responsibilities is never easy. But when you simplify and commit to your new definition of success without apology, you will find it easier to swing your focus towards the right course.

Take a close look at your commitments. Declutter. Remove all the commitments and standing appointments that do not lead you to the right direction. It is a sure way to create a slower, richer and sweeter breathing space in your life.

Find simplicity in your life. Commit only to what is important. Allow yourself margin in your life. You will feel great relief and joy in this precious space. The space promises room. It gives you time for people you love. It gives you the chance to find great things and other treasures you have previously set aside in your busyness.

Create a Simple but Effective Time Management System

After you have settled on your top priorities, establish a time-management system that fits your lifestyle. It can be a paper planner, a digital calendar, or a big dry-erase or wall-based calendar – anything that works for you and your family.

Keep things simple. An easy-to-use, practical, and minimal planner that includes your tasks, appointments, and meals works best.

Commit to making use of this system day after day. It is not enough to plan out your schedule; you have to commit to using it. Check the planner every morning and keep it accessible and regularly updated. Review your upcoming appointments and familiarize yourself with the tasks scheduled for the day.

Establish a routine with day-to-day chores. Assign chores for members of the family. Write these assignments down on post-its and post them on the refrigerator where everyone can see them easily. Doing this eases the pressure of having to constantly remind everybody about their assignments.

Approach the schedules in your life with grace. Schedules may go awry. They do not have to be perfect all the time. Think of a system as a structure, not for achieving perfection, but for being able to live a richer and more joyful family life.

5. Simplified Finances - Getting a Handle on Money

Do you cringe every time you think about handling finances?

The author shares that she was not a numbers girl herself. . After she got married, though, she realized that financial success does not simply depend on curtailing spending and hoping that things work out for the best. It depends on being able to stay on top of your finances and knowing exactly where your money goes.

Reducing Financial Anxiety

Closing your eyes to reality will not work when it comes to finances. You have to take the proverbial bull by its horns. When you finally decide to get a handle on your money, you will be surprised at how simply it can be made to be.

These simple steps will help to lessen financial anxiety and achieve financial freedom.

1. Train yourself to become a numbers person.

2. Establish and use a workable financial system for your family.

3. Engage the services of a trusted advisor.

4. Cut debts.

5. Use one system for expenses.

Regardless of your circumstances, you will discover that if you apply these simple rules, you will find the financial aspect of life simpler, clearer, less difficult and less complicated.

Become a Numbers Person

Become familiar with basic financial terms. Know your family's income, debts, and savings. Create a financial plan that is solid and workable. You can read, ask questions, and educate yourself so that you can discuss business finances with your husband and know what it takes for your family to enjoy a healthy financial picture.

Work Out a Financial System

The author relates that she and her husband look at their finances as two important types – day-to-day and big picture. While they are both involved in all financial planning, discussions, and decisions, her husband handles the big-picture, long-term financial aspects while she manages the day-to-day aspects. He takes care of the kids' educational funds, their retirements, and their investments. She, as work-from-home mother, finds it convenient to check the mail, pay the bills, and monitor their daily expenses.

Deciding how to address each aspect of your financial picture -- and who takes responsibility for what, is essential for coming up with a simplified financial plan that will serve your family well.

Get Expert Help

A trusted advisor helps in planning for and navigating long-term financial objectives. The author says that they have an advisor who advises them about college planning for their kids and about their retirement plans. They confer with him about buying a home or other similar big decisions. He recommends what insurance they should take and what investments they should make.

Getting someone you trust to help you with your financial decisions will help to simplify your finances.

Decrease Debts

Having a simplified financial picture can be life-changing. When you decrease your debts, you immediately improve your financial picture. Pay off your debts as soon as you can so you can enjoy brighter opportunities for financial growth.

With focus, you CAN substantially decrease your debts. There are many things you can do to help you do this. The author says that they spent two years going without vacations, date nights, and extra expenses intentionally to decrease their debt. It was a grueling time in their lives. But when they were able to diminish their debt to a great extent, it was like decluttering. It was like getting rid of junk that was exhausting and draining them of energy.

Create a System for Handling Expenses

The author says that she and her husband use a card for their monthly expenses, including travel, daily expenses, and even some utilities. This enables them to check all their expenses for the month with just a simple login. At the end of each month, they pay off the card in its entirety. This is a simplified way of limiting their monthly expenses to the cash they have at the bank. At year's end, they get a summary which helps them review their expenses and look for areas in which they can curtail their spending.

Some people prefer to spend cash to cover their expenses. This method helps them stick to their budget.

The Dave Ramsey envelope system is another method which you may find effective. You divide your money into actual envelopes and draw from these envelopes to pay for your expenses. The system limits your expenses because you see the cash available reduce with every expense you make.

Involve your Children

You do your kids a great favor when you help them develop the right habits and attitudes towards money at an early age.

Establish an allowance system for them. Help them develop a give-spend-save mentality by teaching them to separate their money into jars or envelopes as soon as they receive it.

Assign a big bottle as a family savings jar where everyone can put in their spare change.

Involve your kids in making decisions like shopping for groceries or planning vacations. Explain to them the financial aspects for making your choices.

When you take control of your finances, you reduce financial worries. You stay in control. This allows you more space and time that you can more joyfully spend in other areas of your life.

6. Simplified Hospitality - Serving and Loving Others Well

Hospitality is an act of service and love that results in making others feel cherished and loved. It is a way of wrapping people in loving care and affection in meaningful, simple, and non-elaborate ways.

Showing Hospitality

Serving others is a privilege. Jesus loved and honored his disciples by washing their feet. He had the heart and attitude of a servant.

You can find simple and meaningful ways to love and serve the people dear to your heart. You can make people feel loved. You can tweak your attitudes and actions in order to be more hospitable – to love people and show them that you care.

How can you show your hospitality to others, using the space, time, and resources that you have?

Serving and Loving your Spouse

A marriage has to survive chaotic finances, disordered routines, and an excess of physical possessions and clutter.

When you are able to simplify these aspects of your life, you are able to strengthen your marriage and give it order and unity.

You have to cultivate the heart of a servant to simplify and make your marriage work. Put your spouse's interests before your own. Seek ways to serve. Give without expecting anything in return. These attitudes allow respect and love to thrive.

How can you serve your spouse well? How can you make him feel loved? How can you be good role models to your children?

- Make your marriage take precedence.

Your marriage is the foundation of your family. It needs to be cared for and tended. Make time for date nights with your spouse. Make your kids know that your relationship with their father is a priority.

- Show your love to your spouse in ways that he understands and prefers.

People feel loved through different ways. Some find joy when given words of appreciation or affirmation. Some delight in receiving presents no matter how simple and inexpensive. Others delight in being shown acts of service. Find out how your spouse wants to be loved – and demonstrate your love for him in that manner.

- Speak in soft gentle tones.

You can cut deeply with your words. You can also use words to uplift, honor, and show care and affection.

Serving and Loving your Children

Children, even if they are born to and raised by the same parents can be vastly different from each other. God shapes each child with distinct strengths and limitations.

You can love and serve your kids in two specific ways. One, you can intentionally craft shared family memories. Two, you can nurture the heart of each child by sharing quality time with him. These two simple ways are essential to raising loving, happy, and strong adults.

Try to look back on your own childhood memories to find ways to help you achieve these goals.

The following are some simple and low-key ideas for making wonderful family memories:

- Having Friday pizza parties

- Making Saturday nights movie night for the family

- Enjoying hot cinnamon rolls for Sunday breakfast

- Preparing and enjoying big Sunday dinners

- Waking up to balloons and cake with candles to blow on birthdays

The following are simple ideas for enjoyable one-on-one time with each kid:

- Going on errands

- Getting staples from the grocery store

- Walking the dog around the neighborhood

- Sharing bedtime prayers

- Reading a book one chapter at a time at bedtime

- Visiting at school and having lunch together

- Going on an evening date in a special restaurant

- Writing loving notes and putting them in lunch boxes

Serving and Loving Friends and Guests

Make your friends feel special by always remembering their

birthdays and other special occasions. Use a perpetual calendar to write down important dates. Keep pretty generic congratulations and birthday cards and pre-stamped envelopes in an accessible tin so you set yourself up to succeed in this endeavor.

Make friends who drop by to visit and stay the night feel special through simple and inexpensive ways. You can stock simple items like bottles of water, clean towels, toiletries, a small cup for a toothbrush, a pretty dish for jewelry, and a pretty piece of paper with the Wi-Fi password on a small tray in the guest room.

Being hospitable means taking the time to anticipate your guests' needs and providing them with the simple amenities to make them feel welcome and comfortable.

Get your friends to come over on weekends to share stories, enjoy movies, or prepare a special meal to share. Create fun experiences together. Have the kids do fun games or work on an artsy project.

These warm, enjoyable, and fun occasions form the good stuff of life. They are the moments which forge

your marriage, shape your children, and strengthen your friendships.

7. Simplified Technology - Creating Healthy Tech Boundaries and Corralling Gadgets

Simplifying life today requires that you take a close look at your use of technology.

Simplifying Technology

There are many easy ways to simplify your use of technology.

- Declutter.

Get rid of technology gadgets that you do not use.

- Simplify your computer, Smartphones, and tablets.

Gadgets can be very useful. However, do not allow them to add clutter to your life. Do not allow them to distract you from what really matters.

Look through your gadgets and delete everything that you do not use, including apps, text chains, old photos, and contacts. Organize similar apps into folders -- utilities, social media, finances, travel, and the like. Keep your home screen simple and neat. Remove apps that you do not use daily.

- Organize your digital files.

You can use your hard drive or Dropbox or iCloud to do this.

Organize your files by category. Keep all videos in one folder, photos in another, and documents in another. You can use Dropbox if you want to connect files from all your devices – tablets, smartphones, and computers.

- Manage and enjoy your photos.

Store your digital photos in folders that are sorted according to year. At the end of each year, choose your favorite photos and use ArtifactUprising.com to make a physical family yearbook.

Do the same with the videos and photos on your phone. Do not let them just sit there.

- Be in control of your e-mail.

Do not allow your inbox to overwhelm you. Use a trash or flag system. Flag all e-mail that you want to take action on or to respond to. Delete the others. Tackle your "flagged" folder when you have the time.

Deal with useless promotional e-mails by "batch unsubscribing" using systems like Unroll.me. Digital clutter is clutter you need to get rid of.

- Update passwords.

Minimize risks of hacking and identity theft. Use strong passwords with the help of Keeper or a similar program. Update passwords every so often.

- Use peaceful computer wallpaper.

Set the tone when you work on your computer with computer wallpaper that helps get you in the right mood when you start work on your computer.

- Turn off notifications.

Every notification calls for your attention. It distracts you and renders you helpless.

If something really warrants your attention, your phone will ring. Do not allow notifications – be they text messages, social media, or e-mail, to interrupt your focus. You do not want to jump up from an important task every time your device demands your attention. Break the addictive habit by turning off notifications.

Technology and Privacy

Technology has affected lives deeply. Everybody now lives in a constantly connected and plugged-in world.

How pervasive is social media in your life and in your children's lives?

Social media can impose great power over your family's lives if you allow it to. You need to set guidelines. You need to set boundaries. If you want to keep your privacy sacred, you have to simplify your family's use of social media.

You do not have to publicly share every little thing that happens in your life. You tend to lose your sense of intimacy and the sacredness of friendships and relationships if you do so.

You should be able to savor interactions, experiences and special moments. You should be able to tuck special moments deep in your heart and cherish them in private in order to keep them special.

Technology is not bad per se. It helps to make life easier. However, the connectedness that technology provides can also be addictive. It can suck time and attention away from things that matter most.

You want to live a joyful and meaningful life. In order to do this, you have to simplify your life and remove distractions which keep you from your goal.

Simplifying life today involves waging the technology battle every day. You have to create a framework for media management. You have to set limitations. You have to do these things for yourself, as well as for the other members of your family, especially your children.

8. Simplified Self - Taking Care of Yourself First and Foremost

Working towards a simplified self is an extremely difficult endeavor.

How do you work on your heart, your confidence, your emotions, and so many other areas to make them simple so that your exterior reflects a calm and peaceful you inside?

How do you even find the time from your responsibilities to your husband, your kids, your work, and your home, to fill your own well – the life spring from where your every effort flows?

Remember though that if you do not take the time to replenish that well you will become empty. You will find it difficult to tend to your obligations the way you hope to.

Take comfort from the fact that simplifying is not an end. It is a continuing journey. You can complete your initial decluttering process. However, you have to constantly do maintenance to maintain your space's initial transformation.

How do you simplify yourself? How do you find inner peace? How do you refill your well?

It pays to take a close look at what makes you feel anxious and overwhelmed -- at what causes you to lose your sense of balance.

A woman carries the world on her shoulders. YOU carry the world on your shoulders. You were created as server to offer your resources to make things easy for other people – your husband, children, parents, siblings, co-workers, friends, and more. You love, care, clean, work, arrange, organize, feed, deal with the minutiae, raise, and nurture. If you want to be an exceptional server, you have to take care of yourself. Make sure that you do not run on empty. Make sure that your well does not become bone-dry.

- Identify your triggers.

What pushes you over the edge? Is it traffic? Is it comparing life with those of your friends as you scroll through their Facebook accounts? Is it the witching hour between dinnertime and bedtime?

- Identify your triggers and do something about them.

Farm out, eliminate, and avoid what you can. If this is not possible, tone down the triggers so they become less powerful. When you face the rush hour on your way to the office, turn on your favorite audio book. Put on dance music and do a little wiggle as you prepare dinner. Identify and alleviate the triggers to calm your soul and heart.

- Give your brain some space.

The previous chapters have shown you the importance of having an empty shelf, getting some breathing room, and pitting margin on your calendar. Give your brain the space that it needs. It is important for the brain to stay still, calm, quiet, and even a little bored at times.

Get out of the mind-set that you have to fill every little space. You do not have to fill every little space in your closet, your calendar, or your mind. If you do so, you will suffocate. You will have no space left to move, breathe or savor special moments in.

If your mind is on over-drive – constantly planning, worrying, comparing your life with those of your friends, and being anxious, you will leave no space for joy or serenity. You will burn out. If you see yourself on this track, take the measures necessary to get off it.

- Slow down.

You can decide to slow down. You can decide to embrace simplicity. If you are constantly overwhelmed, you can take the steps to make practical physical changes so you can live your life the way you want to. You are in control -- whether you want to live your life really happy, a bit happy, or not happy at all. If you enjoy taking your coffee sweet and creamy in an enormous round mug, you can decide to get rid of all the little mugs that clutter up your kitchen. You can choose to embrace the things that bring your heart pure unadulterated joy.

- Take care of your body.

Practical self-care requires you to take care of your body. Nourish, strengthen, monitor, and maintain it in a way that gives it health and vigor. Being healthy allows you to get through your day with vigor and inspiration. It brings inner peace.

Schedule and go to for regular physical check-ups. Schedule visits twice a year, preferably at the same time every year to help you remember them.

Get enough water. Drink 8 to 10 glasses a day.

Get moving. You need to engage in aerobic exercise 20 to 30 minutes a day (or at least thrice a week). You do not have to do lengthy complicated workouts or get gym membership to do this. Simplify. You can get the exercise that you need by taking your dog and your children on a brisk walk several times around the block every afternoon. This way you get the kids out of the house to enjoy some fresh air, talk about their day, and get your body moving at the same time.

Make your body feel cared for. Most women feel good when they get their eyebrows tweezed, their nails filed and polished, their legs shaved, or their hair conditioned. These may be simple (and inexpensive) things yet they make you feel pampered – and self-confident. Set aside time to do these things.

Eat well. Look at the food you eat and notice how they affect your body. Does a certain food make you feel bloated or shaky? Eliminate that from your diet. Does a certain food make you feel energized and in high spirits? Eat more of that. You will probably find out that fresh fruits, vegetables, whole, grains, lean meats, and a lot of liquid belong to the second category. Do not forget to add a handful of joyful foods like warm coffee, dark chocolate, tortilla chips with fresh salsa, and cold tangerines.

- Allow habit and predictability to make your life simpler and easier.

You do not have to bend over backward every single time to do regular things. You do not have to constantly reinvent the wheel. If you and your family love having the same food for breakfast or lunch, you can simply rotate your favorite food options each week and still have nutritious and enjoyable meals. Meals have to be nutritious and palatable. They do not have to be fancy or require a lot of work. Remember that routines reduce the need (and stress) to make decisions.

- Look for little tricks that help you simplify your life.

Figure out the things that drain and overwhelm you. Delegate, lessen, or eliminate them. Look for the things inspire and fuel you. Put them in, embrace them, and do them. You are worthy of love and pampering. Find the space and time to nurture your body, mind, and heart.

9. Simplified Motherhood – Discovering Grace in a Deeply Important Role

There is no such thing as a magical parenting formula. Every family is unique. In fact, every CHILD is unique. It is even doubtful if you can really simplify motherhood. Motherhood and simplify are two words that do not seem to go together at all.

However, with love in your heart and the right attitude, you CAN manage the chaos that comes with raising children. You CAN infuse grace, order, and structure into your family.

The author shares some things that worked with her family. You can choose and pick what systems you think will apply to your own family.

- Learn to manage stuff and cultivate an attitude of gratitude and contentment.

You want to provide your children with everything that they need. When you do not pay attention, however, you may end up putting more time for tending to and picking up stuff rather than relishing your time with the family. You need to simplify your spaces. You need to be able to provide your children with the stuff that they need without going overboard and drowning in stuff.

- Keep the quantity at a minimum.

Kids do not need buckets of clothes and toys. If you go through your kids' toys, you will discover that they play only with a few favorite ones on a regular basis. The rest stays unnoticed and simply fill up precious space. They just add to the clutter and mess.

The author shares that she removed about 75% of the toys from her kids' bins and they did not even notice.

Go through your kids' play area and discard all the board games with incomplete pieces, multiples, broken toys, and things that your kids have outgrown.

Keep the toys that your kids love, especially those that require them to use their creativity and critical thinking skills and develop their motor skills.

You can stop the toy explosion that most homes suffer from. Think about giving experiential gifts like tickets to the aquarium, passes to the movies, or an art set. Some of these gifts may still take up space; however, they are likely to be more purposeful.

Managing the number of toys does more than just make

space. It helps your children develop deeper appreciation, contentment, and a sense of gratitude for what they have.

- Spend quality time with your kids.

Make sure that you spend time playing with your kids. They are likely to have a more enjoyable time playing with you – using the playing cards or board games that they already have than have you come home with new toys for them to play with on their own.

- Teach your kids to pick up after themselves.

Encourage your kids to get one toy and return it after playing with it before picking another one to play with. This teaches them to focus and clear up after themselves.

Involve your kids in everyday age-appropriate chores. Train them to pick up their toys. Allow them to help fold the laundry. Let them set the table. Make them responsible for seeing to it that that the things in their bedrooms are stored properly in the closets.

Making them help out teaches them that tidiness is important. It teaches them that chores are an integral part of living. It teaches them the values of discipline and responsibility.

- Establish family rules.

Teach your kids at a young age to remember and behave according to rules that help them develop the essential virtues. Teach them to listen attentively. Teach them to treat other people with kindness. Teach them to use manners. Teach them to love big. Discuss these rules with them in terms that they can understand and appreciate.

You can think about your own personal family rules and write them down on a chalkboard. Your kids will find it fun to come up with their own mottos representing the values that you are trying to instill in them.

Your kids will face emotional challenges. It is your job as a parent to nurture their hearts and teach them simple life lessons so that they are able to steer successfully through these challenges.

- Tame tantrums and tempers.

How do you deal with the inevitable displays of defiance and temper tantrums that your kids are likely to display every now and then?

Learn to connect with your kids even before the tempers erupt. Learn to redirect their emotions. Kids do not go on tantrums simply to defy or taunt you. Most of the time, they do so because they do not know how to appropriately express what they feel.

If you are in a toy store and your kid temperamentally insists on having you buy him a toy which you think is inappropriate for him to play with, try to redirect his attention away from the source of conflict.

Get down to his level. Get down on your knees and work with your kid as he tries to cope with the emotional moment. Hold him on your lap, speaking in a soft and soothing voice, and simply wait for calmness to descend. When the tempest has passed, explain the situation to your kid in firm and loving tones.

- Make sure that you and your spouse are on the same page.

You and your husband have to demonstrate a unified and consistent front when handling situations.

- Pray randomly with your kids.

Aside from saying prayers with them at bedtime, make it a habit to pray with them in random situations. Pray with them when you see an accident on the highway. Pray with them when a friend can't show up for play date because he is sick. Pray with them when you enjoy particularly scrumptious dish in a restaurant. This beautiful exercise helps to strengthen their faith. It teaches them that regardless of the situation, God is always there to listen to them.

Experiences which may seem ordinary at first glance are often significant in building trust and character. Affirm your kids' feelings. Correct their mistakes gently but firmly. Celebrate their emotional triumphs.

"Keep in mind that a good parent raises adults, not children." This is what the author's dad often tells her. And it has helped her direct her efforts, especially during the times when parenting seems exhausting.

10. Simplified Faith - Connecting Daily with What Matters

Try to go over Psalm 46:10 ESV now and again, especially when life seems to overwhelm you. The author shares that she feels God's presence most strongly when she is able to attain true simplicity and biblical stillness.

Tragedy strikes; this brings you to your knees and makes life suddenly seem so simple. Someone you love becomes seriously ill; your priorities come into laser focus.

You do not have to wait for difficult life changes to appreciate simplicity and make it happen. You can embrace the possibilities that simplicity offers. You can commit to living your life simply. You can declutter your life, commit to less, narrow down life to what is essential – and make precious space for God.

God is there all the time. But when you consciously make space for Him, you are able to feel His presence strongly. When you make Him the center of your life, you are able to hear His words much more clearly.

You can take a simple approach to your life of faith – an approach that is more beautiful and more powerful because of its simplicity.

Love with kindness and mercy. Act justly. Walk in humility with the Lord.

The author shares that she was born and raised in a family that had deep and abiding faith. In time of high-risk pregnancies, great difficulties and tragedies, she felt her faith grow even stronger – and somehow, simpler.

She now realizes that all of us have the opportunity to feel this same particular nearness to God even during ordinary days.

God longs for a rich and intimate relationship with all of us. And He has shown us what genuine God-like love is. He has demonstrated this to us through His Son, Jesus Christ.

However, we are sometimes deterred from seeing how we can love the way God does by the clutter that we allow to fill our lives.

We search for affirmation – and find it in social media. We bask in the number of "likes" we get. We size ourselves up by constantly comparing ourselves with other people.

Many of us have allowed our lives to revolve around social media platforms. We live our lives for others to see how we do so – in social media. We put an enormous degree of importance in how many followers and likes we get. How did we get ourselves in this messy situation?

Twitter, Instagram, Facebook, and other social media platforms have taken such a great space in people's lives. A lot of individuals seem helpless; many feel the urge to put their special intimate lives out in the open for everybody to see. They even take special effort to "curate" what they put out there. They want everybody to believe that they live the perfect lives – just as they think other people do, based on what they, too, put out on these platforms. Everybody seems to be trying to measure up to everybody else – and becoming more disenchanted and unhappy in the process.

Each of us is unique. God gave each one unique looks, talents, gifts, and circumstances. With what we do on social media, however, we are telling God that we do not want to be special. We want to be what we think the world wants us to be.

What we see on social media is not always genuine. They do not represent a person's actual life; they are simply moments captured on film. We have to learn to take back the power that we have given to social media. We have to go back to what is real – and to our God who waits to affirm us and give us guidance in the manner that we hunger for.

Make it a habit to commune with God. Share with Him what fills your heart through simple, direct, and personal prayer.

Sometimes you will find it difficult to express yourself. At other times, the words simply spill over. Regardless of how you communicate with Him, You feel His presence when you give yourself the time and space to sit in silence with Him. You feel connected with Him. This connectedness uplifts your spirit. It gives you life.

God does not require a complicated or formal relationship. He just wants you to allow yourself the space to give Him your heart every day.

A busy, highly-motivated, and task-oriented woman often wants to steer her own way toward what she thinks is an ideal life. The author narrates how it seemed like she spent an entire year in a grueling attempt to raise her three young kids and to maneuver her business into a huge success. It was draining. She knew something had to go.

She prayed and listened hard to what God had to say. She finally opted to allow Him control of her life. She narrates how she and her husband made the drastic decision to remove their highly successful products from almost 800 retail stores all over the world. It was a radical move – one which they were able to do only with a lot of prayer and faith.

She says that she still has her hands full with managing her brand and online store. However, her life seemed to suddenly open up and hold much promise. She now has space to love, think and be creative once more. She got herself to stop considering the numbers on paper. Everything now seems unbelievably new and fresh. She embraces the life that God has led her toward. All it took was for her to take the time to listen and to put her trust in God.

Make space for faith. Let faith underwrite all your decisions. Ask for God's grace when you feel overwhelmed, scared, or weak. Celebrate all your victories with Him.

Make a conscious effort to get to know Him. Make it a point to carve out time and space to read your devotionals and say your prayers. As you go through your day, think about the Scripture and feel joy and serenity. The more you do this, the closer you will feel to Him. You will feel his strong presence in every small aspect of your life.

The author shares show she and her husband make it a point to pray with their children. They want their kids to grow up with the same joy and serenity. They want them to live a life that is rooted in gratitude, contentment, and love -- a life that can only come when one makes faith a priority.

Epilogue

There is so much in life to savor and enjoy. You can have a more satisfying life if you make space for it.

You have to declutter. You have to strip your calendar, your home, and your mind and heart of everything that is not essential. You have to make room. You have to make space. It is only when you have this space that you can see and appreciate what is truly special in your life.

Simplifying your life gives you room to relish a spur-of-the-moment coffee date with your sister. It gives your heart freedom to focus with joy and intent on building blocks with your toddler.

Do not aspire for perfection. Aspire, instead, to live a good life – one that brims over with joy and love.

Acknowledgments

The author acknowledges people important to her life:

She thanks Bryan, her husband, for his whole-hearted love and encouragement. She thanks him for his strength and stability in the crazy and incredible life they share.

She thanks her mom whom she says was her best example. She says that she has a life that is whole and full because of her mom's great love and confidence.

She thanks her dad for teaching her that efficiency can come cloaked with love. She says that she learned from her dad early on that a home that is well-run is a home that has more space for love and fun.

She thanks Brett and Taylor for the love they have showered on her family.

She thanks her team for making work fun. She says it was an incredible honor to work with them.

She says she hopes that Brady realizes exactly how much he is loved. And thanks him for being so kind and brave and smart.

She also thanks Tyler and Monkey for making her world go round with their "squeezes."

She expresses her love to Caroline, her little girl. She says that God made Caroline kind and sweet just as He made her strong and bold. She hopes that when the time comes for Caroline to run her own sweet little home, she will find the time to go over this book and remember how dearly she was loved and adored.

The author also expresses her to gratitude Hannah, as well as to her MTH gals – Kristin, Rhi, Gina, Lara, Amber, and Nancy -- and thanks them for their friendship and prayers.

She thanks Gina Zeidler for the wonderful photos that capture the love and quirks that fill their home.

She thanks Claudia, her agent, for her confidence and her presence during this journey,.

She also thanks her book team at Thomas Nelson – Stefanie, Mandy, Mackenzie, Mike, Jen, Laura M. and everyone else for allowing her to write not Perfection, but Grace. She thanks them for the friendship, support, creativity, and talent that helped make her dream a reality.

Conclusion

Reading this book leaves you with key take-away points.

Chapter 1 highlights the need to simplify your space. You have to declutter. You have to eliminate the excessive stuff that you have accumulated. They do not only take up physical space; they are distractions. T

Stuff overwhelm you by their presence and distract you from focusing on the things that really matter. If you want to have a simplified and much more meaningful and gratifying life, you have to start by freeing up space by getting rid of clutter.

Chapter 2 continues to guide you through the steps of simplifying your life by giving you tips on how to set up a beauty routine that combines simplicity, ease, and convenience. You can streamline your wardrobe and beauty routine. You can come out with a polished and easy signature style that not only leaves you confident but gives you more time to do meaningful work and enjoy the pleasures that life has to offer.

Chapter 3 offers techniques for taking the stress out of meal planning and preparation. It offers helpful tips so you can prepare meals without stressing too much about it. It gives out pointers on what you can do to make mealtimes an opportunity for the entire family to relax, bond, and have fun together.

Chapter 4 points out the sense in reviewing your schedule and looking for activities that you should discard. It underscores the need to be discerning – to choose to do only the things which make your life more joyful or meaningful – and to set the others aside. It points out that it is important to clear space in your calendar. Having this space enables you to clear your mind and helps you to truly focus on what is important.

Chapter 5 makes you realize the importance of being a numbers person so that you are able to understand and do something about your finances. It points out that if you know exactly what your personal financial picture is – and have a clear plan about how to be financially independent, you are better able to eliminate the financial anxiety that most people seem to experience.

Chapter 6 talks about simplified hospitality – and how you can engage in acts of love and service to make other people's lives lighter and happier. It stresses that your loving deeds need not be elaborate. You can make your spouse, children, family and friends feel special through simple acts of kindness and thoughtfulness.

Chapter 7 points out the need to simplify life by removing technological distractions that tend to keep you from enjoying the things that really matter. It points out the growing addiction to social media. It suggests ways for you to draw up a framework of rules to help your family curtail the compulsive use of gadgets and social media.

Chapter 8 tells you to take practical self-care steps to keep you from exhausting your reserves of strength and joy. It tells you to free up space and not go on over-drive. It tells you to make a conscious effort to do what needs to be done so that you do not drown in the multitude of things you have to plan, organize, worry about, and work on. It reminds you that it is important to carve out some "me time" so that you are able to breathe and rejuvenate yourself.

Chapter 9 points out that the everyday experiences that you go through to raise your kids have a lasting impact on them. They strengthen your relationship, build character, and foster trust. It provides techniques to help you teach your kids lessons that will help them become good adults and help them find their way through the challenges that they are going to face later in life.

Chapter 10 focuses on the need to develop your relationship with God. It highlights the importance of making space for

God and for carving out time to talk and listen to Him. It points out that when you make God a priority, you are likely to live a happier, more serene and grace-filled life.

Final Thoughts

Hey! Did you enjoy this book? We sincerely hope you thoroughly enjoyed this short read and have gotten immensely valuable insights that will help you in any areas of your life.

Would it be too greedy if we ask for a review from you?

It takes 1 minute to leave 1 review to possibly influence 1 more person's decision to read just 1 book which may change their 1 life. Your 1 minute matters and we value it and thank you so much for giving us your 1 minute. If it sucks, just say it sucks. Period.

FREE BONUS

P.S. Is it okay if we overdeliver?

Here at Abbey Beathan Publishing, we believe in overdelivering way beyond our reader's expectations. Is it okay if we overdeliver?

Here's the deal, we're going to give you an extremely valuable cheatsheet of "Accelerated Learning". We've partnered up with Ikigai Publishing to present to you the exclusive bonus of "Accelerated Learning Cheatsheet"

What's the catch? We need to trust you… You see, we want to overdeliver and in order for us to do that, we've to trust our reader to keep this bonus a secret to themselves. Why? Because we don't want people to be getting our exclusive accelerated learning cheatsheet without even buying our books itself. Unethical, right?

Ok. Are you ready?

Simply Visit this link: http://bit.ly/acceleratedcheatsheet

Everything else will be self explanatory after you've visited: http://bit.ly/acceleratedcheatsheet

We hope you'll enjoy our free bonuses as much as we've enjoyed preparing it for you!

Free Bonus #2: Free Book Preview of Summary: Daring Greatly

The Book at a Glance

In today's culture, people are more eager to seek success, power, and beauty. Having all of these things makes them feel special. As our nations continue to become industrialized, people, in turn, form higher expectations of each other. Unfortunately, these expectations usually entail sacrifices in terms of vulnerability and empathy. It seems that many are failing to remember that human beings should still be capable of feeling.

In schools, workplaces, and even at home, words that promote positive emotions and social connection are starting to decline. Young people throwing negative expressions toward each other is just another typical conversation we hear on the streets. Many people are not fully aware of how their words or actions can affect another's thoughts and behaviors. It's easy for them to degrade other people just to express their superiority. This leads to softness and vulnerability, once thought of as virtues, to now be perceived as weaknesses.

This book will enlighten you on the subject of shame and vulnerability. The first chapter will discuss the issue of not feeling enough or being enough. We spend a lot of time thinking of the things that we have, what we lack, and then comparing it with everyone else. We strive for perfection because that is what we see in the media. As a result, we feel shame when we feel as if we're not "catching up" to where everyone else is, all based upon the fact that we lack what they currently have.

The second chapter talks about the different myths regarding vulnerability. Sometimes, asking for help is seen as weakness. Instead of respecting this act of courage, we end up letting our fears turn it into a way of judging and criticizing others.

The third chapter will help you further understand shame and how you can resist it. We all experience struggles in life, but when we believe that we're inferior, it will start showing through our behavior. It stops us from recognizing our true strengths as human beings.

Whenever we feel fear or discomfort, we put on different kinds of shields and defenses to protect ourselves, the trouble with which is discussed in the fourth chapter. We are shown there that these forms of protection only make us grow wearier.

In the fifth chapter, you'll learn how protecting yourself from vulnerability can usually lead to disengagement, which is the fundamental problem in our society today. We are not perfect individuals, but we can learn how to engage more and align our values with our actions.

When it comes to education and work, the sixth chapter will discuss the importance of courageous leadership. Being a leader doesn't necessarily mean that you have a high-ranking position or a certain status. It's how you're able to combat shame through honest conversations.

Lastly, the seventh chapter talks about how parents can become good role models to their children by allowing themselves to be more vulnerable. Parenting is not easy and it can become frustrating at times. However, children tend to follow the ways of adults, which is why setting a good example is necessary.

In a world where people are full of expectations, we must not forget that we are still worthy of love and that we are enough. We must find the courage to accept our flaws and develop compassion for others and for ourselves. We live to connect with other people and having that connection is what makes life more meaningful.

Chapter 1

SCARCITY: LOOKING INSIDE OUR CULTURE OF "NEVER ENOUGH"

Once, while Dr. Brené was onstage for one of her talks, a member of the audience asked her why plenty of kids today think of themselves as special. A state of mind which, they say, often leads to narcissism. Here, the word was used as an all-inclusive label for other people's arrogant or rude behavior.

In connection with this thought, research was conducted to analyze several of the current most popular songs. The research reported a significant inclination toward hatred and narcissism in current and popular music. The words "we" and "us" are used on a smaller degree, while the words "me" and "I" are used on a greater extent. It also showed a reduction in words associated with positive emotions and social connection, as well as a surge in words connected to unfriendly behavior and anger, such as kill or hate.

It seems that we have become a culture full of self-centered people. Nowadays, people are more interested in gaining success, power, and beauty. We became so entitled, that we have deluded ourselves into believing our own superiority even when we really have nothing to contribute and nothing valuable to achieve. We don't have the much needed empathy in order to remain connected and compassionate people.

Sometimes, having an explanation for everything brings us relief. We hold other people responsible for the mistakes we made and we feel good about ourselves after doing so. Cutting the narcissists down in number is what we tend to think as the right cure. It's not important if they are our parents, teachers, our neighbors, or the CEOs of large companies. The reaction is still the same. They still need to be made aware that being special or great is not what matters most in life because chances are, no one would even care what we have accomplished in life.

Narcissism, as a subject matter, has already entered our awareness in such a way that people immediately link it with different behavioral patterns. This includes grandiosity, lack of compassion or empathy, and an extensive demand for approval and admiration.

What people don't completely understand is that the severity of a person's narcissism is actually rooted in shame. This means that trying to fix the problem by cutting down the number of narcissists is not the best solution, nor is it constantly reminding people of their smallness or inadequacies. *Shaming* people isn't the cure. It's what causes these kinds of rude behaviors.

Understanding Narcissism in a Different Way

Pinpointing or labeling people who are struggling due to the things they're accumulating from their environment is often more disastrous to their overall healing rather than being actually helpful. The problem is that it focuses on who people really are instead of the choices they made. Dr. Brené believes that people must be held responsible for their own actions. However, she's not referring to **blaming** them, but pinpointing the main cause of the problems so they can be properly addressed instead.

It would be more helpful to identify behavioral patterns and to interpret what they might suggest. Understand how it's completely different from defining oneself by a specific judgment, and how lumping the two together usually intensifies shame and stops people from trying to seek help.

It's important for us to become aware of these influences and trends, but it's more beneficial if we view these behavioral patterns through the "vulnerable standpoint". For instance, when we see someone who's afraid of being thought of as ordinary — we must do our best to remove our biases. We can look at this from a place of empathy and instead, find someone who only wants to be noticed and loved. They're scared that being average would not give them that sense of belongingness or purpose which they desire.

This provides clarity and helps explain the root of the problem, as well as offer practical solutions. Nowadays, it's easy to believe this pervasive idea that our life is purposeless or ordinary simply because it is not expressed almost everywhere we go. We become susceptible to these kinds of messages which lead to destructive behavior, which also results in more pain and creates disconnection. Still, when we feel hurt and when our sense of love and belonging are at risk, we go after those that would give us full security.

The good thing is that, we can always learn something when we think about every information and expectation that determines our society, how these things affect our behaviors, the way our struggles are associated with defending ourselves, and the way they are connected to vulnerability.

Dr. Brené doesn't believe that the world is full of people who are narcissists. Our culture is just influenced by many different and powerful factors that people feel the need to overcompensate and create for themselves, a life that is beyond ordinary.

Scarcity: The Problem of Never Having Enough or Being Enough

Scarcity simply comes with living. It's the issue of "never enough." It flourishes in a society where every person is extremely aware of insufficiency. We always think that we can never be enough. Everything feels limited or inadequate, especially when it comes to love, money, and security. We spend a lot of time thinking about the things we have and the things we lack and then compare everything with everyone else's.

We often compare our lives, families, marriages, or communities with unrealistic pictures of perfection, which are frequently conveyed by the media. But, what we don't realize is that this kind of behavior is completely useless and ineffective towards our own personal growth.

Where Scarcity Begins

Scarcity doesn't seize a particular culture overnight. However, the feeling and idea exist in cultures that are prone to shame and are deeply filled with endless comparison and broken by disengagement.

We live in a world where life hasn't really been easy, but the recent years have brought with them many traumatic events, such as tragic natural disasters, numerous wars, school shootings and other random violence, that created a lot of changes in our society. We have survived, but we are constantly trying to make it through the things that have tattered our idea of security.

Falling into frustration with regards to scarcity is how our culture tries to cope with the stress. It usually begins when we've already been through so many things and instead of uniting to recover and improve, we choose to be angry and end up becoming paranoid.

It takes daily awareness, work, and commitment to develop relationships, raise a loving family, manage a school, or build an organizational system. This culture that surrounds us currently loves to put a pressure on us and if we're not willing to fight or stand up to the things we firmly believe in, we'll only end up suffering in scarcity

One way to prevent being in a state of not having enough is not acquiring everything or living in abundance, but rather living in wholeheartedness by believing that we're enough, we're worthy, and

84

we can be vulnerable. We're all sick and tired of feeling scared. Each of us wants to make a bold and brave movement.

SUMMARY:

Allen Carr's Easy Way to Stop Smoking

30 Years of Helping Smokers to Stop

ABBEY BEATHAN

Legal & Disclaimer

The information contained in this book is not designed to replace or take the place of any form of medicine or professional medical advice. The information in this book has been provided for educational and entertainment purposes only.

The information contained in this book has been compiled from sources deemed reliable, and it is accurate to the best of the Author's knowledge; however, the Author cannot guarantee its accuracy and validity and cannot be held liable for any errors or omissions. Changes are periodically made to this book. You must consult your doctor or get professional medical advice before using any of the suggested remedies, techniques, or information in this book. Images used in this book are not the same as of that of the actual book. This is a totally separate and different entity from that of the original book titled: "Allen Carr's Easy Way to Stop Smoking"

Upon using the information contained in this book, you agree to hold harmless the Author from and against any damages, costs, and expenses, including any legal fees potentially resulting from the application of any of the information provided by this guide. This disclaimer applies to any damages or injury caused by the use and application, whether directly or indirectly, of any advice or information presented, whether for breach of contract, tort, negligence, personal injury, criminal intent, or under any other cause of action.

You agree to accept all risks of using the information presented inside this book. You need to consult a professional medical practitioner in order to ensure you are both able and healthy enough to participate in this program.

Table of Contents

The Book at a Glance

All smokers are aware of the fact that smoking brings about a variety of health issues, yet they can't seem to stop themselves from doing so. Even with the numerous health campaigns advocating against smoking, smokers still can't seem to stop themselves from lighting another cigarette.

In Allen Carr's Easy Way to Stop Smoking, the author provides clear and concise instructions on how a person can end his smoking habit for good. In the first chapter, he talks about his own addiction, how he was able to overcome it, and why he is determined to help others overcome the same.

In chapter two, the author introduces his readers to the Easy Method, which is his way of helping us stop smoking. It also explains why it is different from all other anti-smoking methods. Chapter three discusses the real reasons why smokers find it hard to stop. And in chapter four, the author explains why he thinks smoking is a sinister trap.

Chapter five opens our eyes to the real reasons why we can't seem to stop smoking: nicotine addiction and brainwashing. The author gave us an in-depth discussion on nicotine addiction in chapter six, while chapter seven was all about brainwashing, and how our subconscious mind affects how we perceive things.

In chapter eight, the author introduces us to the five reasons why smokers go back to lighting a cigarette as soon as they experience withdrawal pangs. These are stress, boredom, concentration, relaxation, and a combination of two, more, or all of these reasons. In chapter nine, the author digs deep into why we think we need to smoke when we feel stressed out. But more importantly, he gives us a concrete explanation on why smoking can never relieve our stress.

In chapter ten, the author explains why cigarettes make us feel tired all the time, leading to a false belief that it helps us alleviate boredom. In chapter eleven, the author shatters our false notion that smoking improves our concentration, while in chapter nine, he shares why he thinks smokers are the most unrelaxed individuals on the planet. And finally, chapter thirteen will be a brief explanation as to why smokers think combination cigarettes are the best – and why, in reality, it is the worst.

Chapter fourteen and fifteen makes it clear that when we give up smoking, we don't lose anything. But instead, we gain everything. In chapters sixteen to twenty one, the author provides us with a thorough discussion on how smoking affects our budget, health, energy, and confidence. Chapters 22 to 24 introduces us to the traditional anti-smoking methods, and provides us with explanations as to why they don't work. And finally, chapter 25 to 27 provides us with a breakdown of the different types of smokers.

Beginning from chapter 28 until chapter 31, the author discusses the important factors that we must consider before proceeding with the Easy Way. In chapter 32, the author lays down the two steps involved in the easy method: to commit and to develop a mindset of rejoicing. Chapters 33 to 38 sufficiently provides us with tips and pieces of advice which will help us get through the dreaded withdrawal period.

The breathtakingly beautiful moment of revelation is discussed in chapter 39. And finally, the last part of this book contains final pieces of advice to help us get through the post-withdrawal phase.

Thus, as long as we carefully and consciously follow the instructions laid down in this book, we can be certain that we can finally put an end to our smoking problem. And better yet, we can also serve as an inspiration to others who are also experiencing the same problem.

Introduction

No addiction is untreatable. However, those who suffer from vices tend to believe otherwise – as a result, that belief would prevent them from completely letting go of their nasty ways.

Allen Carr was among those who believed that there was no way out of his chain-smoking ways. He shares that he has tried a lot, if not all, of today's anti-smoking methods. Unfortunately, all of his efforts went down the drain since he would fall back to smoking within months.

Through the author's determination to get rid of this nasty habit, coupled with the support from his wife and loved ones, the author was able to discover the Easy Way out of smoking. To make sure that his method works for everyone, he tried it out with friends first. After receiving their positive feedback, he became determined to share it with the world. And that is the main purpose of this book.

Nonetheless, the author understands that some readers will be skeptic about what he is about to present – after all, most of his readers are the ones who have also failed to escape their slavery to nicotine. But to be truly free, we have to start somewhere. And fortunately, you already took the first step when you picked up this book.

The Worst Nicotine Addict I Have Yet to Meet

Before discussing the main points of the Easy Way, the author wants his readers to understand where he's coming from first.

In this chapter, his shares that he used to be a chain smoker for around thirty years, and that he has already tried all of the known means to get rid of this habit – and all of them to no avail. In fact, he was already on the brink of giving up when his wife encouraged him to see a hypnotherapist.

Despite his skepticism, he still decided to push through with it. Fortunately, the result was promising. He shares that he immediately stopped smoking after the session, and didn't have a hard time during the withdrawal stage.

Nonetheless, he reminds us that hypnotherapy isn't the ultimate answer to end smoking. Since it treats people by suggesting messages, we must be careful with the kind of message that is being sent our way. Otherwise, we can never be free from the smoking trap. Eventually, this led the author to discover the Easy Way to stop smoking.

Throughout reading this book, the author wants us to keep an open mind. After all, quitting itself is easy. The real challenge lies in getting past the withdrawal stage. Fortunately, this book will provide us with clear and concrete instructions on how we can move past that stage.

The Easy Method

Most anti-smoking methods fail because they encourage us to stop smoking at the onset, and then leave us with a strong sense of craving towards getting back on board. In contrast, the method in this book aims to help us develop a mindset first – a mindset that we're already free from the chains of nicotine. And from this, we can gather the strength to actually put an end to smoking.

In order to develop this mindset, we must reflect on the following questions first:

- What is smoking doing to me?

- Am I actually enjoying it?

- Is it necessary for me to keep on smoking throughout my life?

These questions should be enough to give us a wakeup call that smoking does nothing good to our body. Nonetheless, the author acknowledges that there can also be smokers who would try to provide rationalized answers to justify their situation. But if we analyze their answers, we begin to realize that their reasons are all illusions and false beliefs.

Thus, in order to get to the bottom of a person's smoking problems, we must first debunk these fallacies and illusions. Once these are removed from a person's life, he can now focus on the things that truly matter in his life.

Why is it Difficult to Stop?

It may not be obvious, but the fact remains that all smokers wish to quit. They are all aware of the negative effects of smoking, and that terrifies them enough to want to break the habit as soon as possible. The author even shares that a common desire among confirmed smokers is to go back in time to stop themselves from enjoying that first cigarette.

But, despite knowing the hazards of smoking, they can't seem to stop themselves from lighting another cigarette. Quitting is just too difficult.

In order to stop smoking, we must understand why it is so hard to stop in the first place. Numerous organizations campaign against smoking by explaining how and why it is easy to stop. However, these campaigns often fail and cause smokers to fall back to their horrible ways.

In contrast, the Easy Way will help us understand why quitting is hard. The author wants us to understand that our reasons for smoking are all just illusions. He explains each illusion as follows:

- Quitting can create a stronger withdrawal symptom. In a succeeding chapter, we will understand that actual withdrawal symptoms from nicotine are not as powerful as what we have imagined.

- Smoking is enjoyable. There are other things we enjoy, but we never take these other things excessively.

- There are deep psychological reasons. Some people only resort to smoking because they want to exude an image of maturity. Unfortunately, that is not always the result they get.

- Smoking makes a person look macho. Breathing cancerous tars into your system isn't manly at all.

- Smoking relieves boredom. Keep in mind that boredom is only a frame of mind. Besides, there is nothing truly interesting about lighting a cigarette.

- I smoke because my friends smoke. You don't have to do what others are doing. After all, you are the only person in control of your own life.

- Smoking has already become a habit, and habits are hard to break. This is a fallacy. The author shares that in the United Kingdom, drivers formed the habit of driving on the left lane – but they can easily break that habit if they have to drive in countries where right-lane driving is observed.

With all these fallacies and illusions debunked, we can now embrace the real reason why it is so hard to stop smoking: we are addicted to nicotine.

Once we come to fully understand that the real problem is an addiction, dealing with it would be easier. In fact, the author shares that we can fully let go of smoking within three weeks' time.

The Sinister Trap

Smoking is a sinister trap that's hard to escape once you're inside. We are often lured into it because we see smoking adults who always warn us against how disgusting a cigarette is. But since they can't seem to stop smoking, it's hard to believe that they're not enjoying it – and that makes us curious enough to give it a try.

Now, how hooked we become to smoking all depends on that first cigarette. If it tastes awful, then we can confirm to ourselves that we don't enjoy it. We never become hooked. On the other hand, if that first puff tastes amazing, then we've already entered the trap.

The author goes on to add that we only want to exit this smoking trap when life begins to feel more stressful because of it. But as soon as we quit, we experience more stress because we're no longer allowed to depend on that one thing that seems to help us relieve it. And within a span of a few days, we finally give in. We light a cigarette and firmly decide to quit when we're no longer under extreme amounts of stress. Unfortunately, that day never arrives.

But like what has been discussed in the previous chapter, all of this is just an illusion. Keep in mind that no matter how complicated a puzzle may be, it always has a corresponding solution. And this sinister smoking trap is no different.

Why Do We Carry on Smoking?

With all the negative effects of smoking in mind, any logical person would wonder why smokers find it hard to quit. However, smokers are smart and rational individuals. They are aware of all these health risks. They are also aware of how much money they are spending on cigarettes in a year. There's no need to remind them of all of these.

Instead, we must discuss and understand the real reasons why they can't seem to stop. According to the author, there are only two main reasons: nicotine addiction and brainwashing. Each of these reasons will be discussed in detail in the two succeeding chapters.

Nicotine Addiction

Now that we are aware of our true situation, we have to dig deeper into what this nicotine addiction is.

Nicotine is a colorless, oily, and highly addictive compound found in tobacco. When nicotine enters our lungs and into our veins, it provides us with an illusion that it is pleasurable. But this compound immediately leaves the bloodstream within minutes, and that makes the smoker feel withdrawal symptoms.

But at this point, the author wants to make one thing clear with us: these withdrawal pangs are mainly mental. In other words, the pangs you think you feel are all in your head. Unfortunately, the addiction tricks us to think that it's all real.

With these facts in mind, we may still find it hard to believe that we are addicted to nicotine. Fortunately, nicotine is not like other drugs – it is easy to kick out of our system. But before we can do that, we must first accept that we are, in fact, addicted to it.

Accepting that we're nicotine addicts can be hard to swallow. To help us ease into that thought, the author shares the following reasons why acceptance can help us overcome our main problem:

1. We do not see the cigarette as a prop, but as something we actually enjoy. If we accept that we are addicted to it, coupled with the realization that smoking is bad for our health, our eyes become open to reality.

2. Once we accept that we are addicted, we can immediately proceed with getting rid of the nicotine in our body. According to studies, this only takes about three weeks, regardless of how heavy or how long you have been smoking.

Nonetheless, our problem doesn't end with acknowledging our nicotine addiction. According to the author, the real problem lies in being brainwashed by the little nicotine monster. More on brainwashing will be discussed in the succeeding chapter.

Brainwashing and the Sleeping Partner

From everything that has been discussed in the previous chapter, we now come to understand that nicotine addiction stems from brainwashing. In this chapter, the author gives us an in-depth explanation of brainwashing, and how our sleeping partner plays a vital role in it.

Our subconscious mind, which the author refers to as the Sleeping Partner, has a lot to do with our nicotine addiction. The author explains that the power of suggestion plays a starring role in convincing the subconscious mind to make us do something. Unfortunately, advertising and marketing companies know exactly how to use it – and this is exactly what is employed by companies selling cigarette.

Additionally, movies and television shows often portray smokers as confident, macho, and sociable individuals, and this effectively lures us to try smoking. Sometimes, the brainwashing can also stem from our own homes, especially if we have a role model who smokes.

But as early as now, the author wants us to keep in mind that all of these are mere illusions. Smoking only introduces filth and nicotine into our lungs, and that doesn't solve any of our problems. It can't magically transform us into the person we've always wanted to become, and neither can it effectively reduce our stress levels.

Understanding and embracing the fact that we are being brainwashed into smoking can make this process easier than it already is. As long as we continuously remind ourselves that the joys of smoking are all mere illusions, then we remain on the path towards freedom from nicotine slavery.

Relieving Withdrawal Pangs

Back in the early days, when the cigarette was first introduced to society, it was merely considered as a social prop. What people didn't know then was that a single cigarette could subtly lure them towards an addiction that is hard to break free from.

Most smokers tend to believe that the more drawn we become to nicotine, the stronger the withdrawal pangs would become. However, the truth is that withdrawal symptoms from nicotine are so subtle, that smokers only realize that they are addicted to it when they try to stop smoking.

Among the many reasons why smokers go back to smoking after trying to stop is the belief that it helps reduce stress, alleviate boredom, improve concentration, boost relaxation, or a combination of all of these. In the succeeding chapters, the author aims to disprove all of these beliefs.

Stress

The biggest reason why people turn to smoking is the belief that it can reduce their stress levels. To disprove this notion, the author provides us with an illustration.

He shares that for some people, a telephone conversation can be stressful, especially for a businessman who may receive calls from dissatisfied customers, or from his infuriated boss. Because of his anxiety he ends up lighting a cigarette. He doesn't really know why he does it, but it seems to make him feel relieved.

On the contrary, the author explains that the businessman was already experiencing withdrawal pangs, which seems to have aggravated his normal stress levels. By smoking, he relieved his withdrawal stress, which also gives him an illusion that his stress levels went down. Unfortunately, the more a person lights a cigarette, the more stressed he actually becomes, compared to a non-smoker. The author explains this by saying that with every puff of the cigarette, the nicotine becomes less effective in restoring a person's stress levels.

Now, to help us get into the proper mindset, he wants us to visualize that our doctor finally tells us that if we don't stop smoking, he will have to remove our legs. After hearing this, pause for a while and imagine what life would be like without legs. A logical mind would easily choose to give up smoking. But, the heaviest smokers would simply dismiss this visualization and still proceed with smoking. This is what this drug can do to us: it can take away our nerve and courage. It can make us believe that it is our source of strength when, in reality, it is the one that's taking our life away.

So today, make sure to reflect on the fact that the cigarette is not responsible for calming our nerves. Instead, keep on reminding yourself that it is the very reason which is causing our nerves to deteriorate. Once we do so, we regain our confidence and self-assurance, without being dependent on any drug.

Boredom

Boredom is another reason why some people end up smoking. But as previously stated, boredom is a frame of mind. It cannot be alleviated by intoxicating yourself with harmful substances.

The author shares that when we stop smoking, even for just a few minutes, we would feel as if something is missing. If we're busy, we barely realize that we are experiencing withdrawal from the absence of that drug. On the contrary, if we're not doing anything, we end up feeding the nicotine monster.

Additionally, the author also wants to point out that cigarettes can even increase our boredom, since it makes us feel tired – and this makes us lose interest in any other activity. From this, we can see a cycle of lighting a cigarette, feeling bored as a result, and then lighting another cigarette under the false belief that it can alleviate boredom. From the standpoint of a non-smoker, or an ex-chain smoker, nothing is more boring than that of lighting a cigarette over and over again.

Concentration

Another thing we have to hammer into our heads is this: cigarettes do not, and cannot, help improve our concentration.

In reality, we end up lighting a cigarette because the nicotine monster keeps on nagging us to be fed. As soon as he gets his share of the drug, the nicotine monster allows us proceed with what we have to do – that is, until he needs another dose of it.

From this, we can now see that smoking does not improve our concentration at all. If anything, it is actually ruining it. Recall that the more we intoxicate ourselves with nicotine, the less relieved we become over time. Thus, it only makes our situation worse.

Additionally, nicotine blocks our arteries and veins, which makes it difficult to supply the brain with oxygen. As a result, our concentration becomes adversely affected. According to the author, this is the reason why some of the willpower methods don't work. After all, how could a person possibly will himself to stop smoking if the nicotine monster keeps blocking out his concentration?

Before ending this chapter, the author wants us to know that there are no physical withdrawal pangs. Everything is in our heads. If we believe that smoking improves our concentration, then why are there non-smokers who demonstrate great levels of concentration? Ponder on that. Usually, it's the self-doubt that makes it hard to let go.

Relaxation

Smoking does not help anyone relax. In fact, the author shares that nicotine can even make our pulse rate higher.

From what the author has gathered, he can confidently tell us that the most unrelaxed people are those who smoke. If you try to look around, you will notice that smokers are the ones who would easily lose their temper and throw a fit. Unfortunately, the sad part is that they rarely think that there is anything wrong with them.

The author goes on to add that smoking actually tends to rob people of feeling joy. When they think they're beginning to relax because of the cigarette, it is actually the nicotine monster that's calmed down – not you. As soon as you're done with one stick, the monster would want to have another one, and you'll feel agitated all over again. Thus, only non-smokers are capable of experiencing true relaxation.

Combination Cigarettes

According to the author, we resort to combination cigarettes when we experience two, more, or all of the reasons for smoking in one occasion. When we smoke during these situations, we think that it is the only way for us to really enjoy the event and feel relaxed.

Again, everything is all in our heads. However, this is also the type which we think we'll miss most if we have to stop smoking. In our heads, we think that it is something we cannot let go of, since it can drastically improve our lives with just one cigarette.

But that is all an illusion. Keep in mind that the cigarette is only relieving us from withdrawal symptoms. The moment we stopped smoking, we began to feel overwhelmed by pangs of withdrawal, so we are made to believe that the cigarette offered a cure. But in reality, the occasion wasn't as stressful as we thought it was – it was the nicotine monster which made it seem worse.

To let go, we must change our perspective of the combination cigarette. There is absolutely nothing special about it. Instead of helping us enjoy the occasion, we end up less focused on it because the nicotine monster keeps nudging us to go out and smoke. As a result, this makes the event seem stressful, so we never really end up enjoying it.

What Am I Giving up?

To a chain smoker, quitting would feel like giving up everything. But in reality, we are not giving up anything at all. And in return, we gain everything.

Before beginning with this chapter's discussion, the author wants us to keep on reminding ourselves that cigarettes do not fill a void in our lives. On the contrary, they are responsible for creating those voids in the first place.

To explain how smoking creates a void, the author shares that when we smoke during social events, we often think it helps us become more confident and sociable. However, keep in mind that no one really likes the smell of cigarettes. As a result, you try your best to keep the smoke away from the person you're talking to, while also making sure that you dispose of the ash in a manner that won't cause such a mess. The stained teeth and the bad breath doesn't help, either.

Thus, there really is nothing to lose if we give up on smoking. Keep this in mind when you are tempted to light another cigarette.

Self-imposed Slavery

It may be hard to admit, but we are responsible for our own slavery to nicotine. The author shares that most smokers don't usually like their first cigarette, but the brainwashing is so strong, that they end up trying it a second or third time. Unfortunately, by this time, the body now gets a kick from the nicotine, and the slavery starts.

The interesting part about cigarette smoking, however, is that the smoker usually doesn't realize that he is already addicted – that is, until he is forced not to smoke. For example, a smoker may find it stressful when he visits a friend's home, and find that there is no ash tray. This is also the case when he has to socialize with people who are disgusted by the smell of smoke. Because he feels deprived, he becomes agitated and irritable.

From a logical standpoint, not being allowed to smoke shouldn't agitate us. In fact, we should be thankful. However, smokers no longer think that way because the nicotine monster already have them enslaved.

I'll Save £x a Week

Smokers who are doing well in life aren't usually bothered by a slight increase in the price of a pack of cigarette. A pack is usually worth a few bucks, and this doesn't mean anything to an established individual earning thousands per month.

However, if we are to compute the amount they will be spending for a lifetime supply of cigarette, it would cost them up to around £40,000! Unfortunately, smokers rarely realize how much their spending on cigarettes because they never think of it as something they would be dealing with forever – that is, until you try to make them stop smoking.

Thus, the author often tries to make smokers compute how much money he'll be spending on cigarettes if he wouldn't stop today. Once the smoker realizes that the amount is too substantial to be thrown away like that, he will be determined to stop smoking.

Health

Everyone is aware of the health hazards that go hand in hand with smoking. However, bear in mind that smokers are being brainwashed to think that smoking is good for them, so they may not fully comprehend the gravity of its health risks.

The brainwashing is so strong that smokers would rather try to live with much precaution – like making sure that they won't get hit by a bus as they cross the road – but they fail to realize that the bigger threat on their life lies in the fact that they smoke. They become extra keen on making sure that they won't get into physical accidents, and yet they try to poison themselves every day.

Unfortunately, most smokers only consider this as a harmless habit. This is especially true when they don't experience symptoms like coughing yet. But according to the author, the tar from nicotine rarely triggers any symptoms – they just build up in our lungs and become cancer.

Thus, the next time we light a cigarette, think of it as lighting a fuse. The more you light it, the closer the bomb is to exploding. Are you really willing to risk it?

Energy

Another effect of brainwashing is that smokers don't often realize that smoking has taken its toll on their energy levels.

From a scientific standpoint, smoking fills our lungs with tar, which makes us inhale less oxygen. As a result, our brain gets deprived of oxygen and other nutrients, and that can make us lose focus and feel tired all the time. Unfortunately, most smokers think that their constant lack of energy is only due to the fact that they are no longer energetic children.

According to the author, the opposite is true. As we age, we can have the same levels of energy as when we were children. It is only the nicotine monster that is making us feel tired all the time. In fact, he even shares that as soon as he extinguished his last cigarette, he already felt a big impact on his health. He no longer experienced an asthma attack, and his breathing has become less congested. And soon enough, he was able to jog and swim again.

It Relaxes Me and Gives Me Confidence

The author wants to remind us that smoking does not help us relax, and neither does it provide us with a confidence boost. In fact, it can even leave us feeling insecure, especially when we find ourselves running out of cigarettes in the middle of the night.

Thus, the next time we feel the need to smoke in order to relax, we must remind ourselves that we are only being brainwashed. We are only feeding the nicotine monster who is only wreaking havoc inside our body.

Those Sinister Black Shadows

All smokers have a reason for wanting to quit. Among the most common reasons are health and finances. But for the author, one of the biggest reasons would be to get rid of the sinister black shadows that were always lurking at the back of his mind.

According to the author, these sinister black shadows stem from the feeling of being despised by non-smokers. He shares that smokers are aware that people are disgusted by the smell of cigarettes, so they know how displeased non-smokers can be when they see others smoking in public. Because of this, the author also began to feel apologetic towards non-smokers, because he couldn't seem to stop smoking.

Fortunately, he was able to discover the Easy Way, and he was finally able to get rid of these sinister black shadows. Accordingly, this made the biggest impact in his life. He even claims that getting rid of these shadows made him respect himself a lot more.

The Advantages of Being a Smoker

This chapter literally contains nothing – because there really is nothing to gain from being a smoker.

The Willpower Method of Stopping

Smokers often think that they can simply will themselves to stop smoking. However, this method usually fails because we are no longer in control of our own mind. We are now slaves to the nicotine monster.

Additionally, the author also adds that the problem lies in the fact that it takes us too long to recognize that we are already addicted. Smokers who only light up a cigarette or two per day would even laugh at the suggestion. However, if we were to completely take their cigarettes away from them, they'll soon realize that they can't seem to give it up that easily.

Much of the problem with the Willpower Method also lies in the fact that smokers were already brainwashed to think that it smoking is enjoyable. This is the biggest reason why smokers fall back to their old ways during the infamous withdrawal period. But again, this is all just part of an illusion. There is nothing enjoyable about feeding our body with poison.

Fortunately, all this brainwashing only occurs as long as the nicotine monster lives within us. It ends when it is completely flushed out of our system. According to the author, this can last for about three weeks. And the better news is that his Easy Way can help get us through this dreaded period.

Beware of Cutting Down

A majority of smokers believe that cutting down on his cigarette consumption is a great way to eventually end his addiction. However, this can actually make the addiction grow worse.

According to the author, cutting down is bad for smokers because of the following reasons:

1. He is still keeping the nicotine monster alive.

2. Cutting down means that he is desperately waiting for the next time he can smoke, and that is not a good use of his time.

3. This can double his suffering. He deals with life's normal stresses and responsibilities, while also trying to deal with the nicotine monster he's been feeding.

4. On average, smokers who try to cut down end up smoking even more. Lighting and smoking cigarettes became automatic, so they barely realize that they have already finished an entire pack.

Thus, instead of cutting down, the author wants us to fully commit to stop smoking. Reducing our intake will not make it easier for us to stop at all, so there's no point to doing it gradually. All it takes to stop is getting the right frame of mind. More on this topic will be discussed on a later chapter.

Just One Cigarette

All it took for smokers to become hooked is one cigarette. That one cigarette catapulted them into this addiction, and now they find it impossible to escape from the trap.

Every day, the smoker struggles with his promise to smoke just one cigarette. Unfortunately, that one cigarette often starts a chain, which leaves him smoking twenty more cigarettes for the entire day.

Thus, whenever we feel tempted to smoke just one cigarette, the author wants us to think of the lifetime of misery that that one cigarette is going to take us to. Would it be worth it?

To end this chapter, the author lays down the following fundamentals that we should keep in mind:

1. There is nothing to lose if we give up on smoking. Instead, we gain a multitude of advantages.

2. The odd cigarette is just a myth. It does not exist. On the contrary, what exists is a lifetime of poisoning yourself.

3. All smokers, even when one thinks that he is already a hopeless case, can find it easy to stop smoking.

Casual Smokers, Teenagers, Non-smokers

In this chapter, the author wishes to present us with some noteworthy definitions.

- Non-smokers. These are defined as those who were never lured into the sinister trap. Nonetheless, these non-smokers should not be complacent.

- Casual smokers. According to the author, there are

two basic classifications of casual smokers: those who have fallen into the trap but doesn't realize it yet, and those who were former heavy smokers. The author goes on to list down other classifications of smokers under this category, like those who only smoke five cigarettes per day, those who only smoke during the morning or evening, and those who believe that they are merely occasional smokers.

The author believes that those who classify themselves as casual smokers are in the same trouble as those who are heavy smokers. They are trapped in the same puzzle, after all. But to get them to stop, they must first realize that they are already addicted.

The same warning goes for the occasional smoker who thinks that he doesn't like smoking at all. According to the author, all heavy smokers began as occasional smokers. Thus, if the occasional smoker really thinks that he doesn't like it, then he should give up on smoking all at once.

This chapter ends with a warning for parents to not be complacent in raising their children. If they see that children are disgusted by the smell of cigarette, that doesn't automatically mean that they will grow up as non-smokers. They should make sure that there will be no place for brainwashing as they grow up, especially when they become teenagers. After all, teenagers are the hardest to convince that they need treatment, especially when they are filled with that youthful energy and health.

The Secret Smoker

The Secret Smoker falls under a special category. According to the author, these are the smokers who were banned from smoking, but their craving is so strong so they look for ways to smoke without being caught.

This kind of smoker will find ways just so they can get a taste of the cigarette. The author shares that when he used to be a secret smoker, he would mindlessly cause an argument just so he can storm out of the house and light a smoke. On other occasions, he would volunteer to buy a minor item, take a smoking break, and then return home hours later. It was so obvious that he was trying to sneak a smoke, and it ended up making him feel a little antisocial.

Looking back on his experiences, the author also recalls how restless he was during that phase. He was constantly worrying that his wife would find his hidden stash of cigarette. He was in constant fear that he would reek of the smell of cigarette. Eventually, this caused him to lose his self-respect. And he doesn't want this to happen to you.

A Social Habit?

A common myth surrounding cigarette smoking is that it is a social habit. However, the opposite is true. Smokers themselves admit that they find it rather antisocial.

With the help of mass media and information technology, more and more people are becoming aware of the hazards of smoking and inhaling second-hand smoke. This makes non-smokers loathe those who smoke in public, and smokers end up feeling guilty and apologetic. As a result, they try not to smoke during social events, and this only leaves them feeling deprived. This causes smokers to scurry off to a distance where they can be away from people and smoke in peace.

For most smokers, this is enough reason for them to give up on smoking completely. And fortunately, an increasing number of smokers are quitting on a daily basis. Do you really want to be the last one to stay on a sinking ship?

Timing

Having the determination to finally stop smoking is a noble gesture. However, there is also another factor that we must take into consideration: timing.

This doesn't mean that we have to find the right time when we should quit. If we do so, then the answer would obviously be "now".

However, all the brainwashing is making us believe that the right time to quit is when we are not too stressed. But let's get real: all of us experience stress on a daily basis. When we promise to quit when we're no longer stressed, it's like we're making a promise to never quit at all.

Thus, the author wants us to fight off the brainwashing. There is no perfect timing for quitting. We have to quit now.

Will I Miss the Cigarette?

The answer to this question is a resounding "no".

The author guarantees that as soon as we kill off that little monster and successfully flush it out of our system, then we would be free from any form of temptation. After all, we all know how horrible smoking is, so the only logical explanation for all that craving is that it is the work of the nicotine monster.

Additionally, the author wants us to remember that smokers don't deserve our envy. Think about it: smokers consume thousands of pounds a year on something that is poisoning them. Do we really want to envy someone who lives like that? Absolutely not. If anything, we should pity them instead.

Will I Put on Weight?

This is another myth that the author wishes to bust. Keep in mind that smoking drains our confidence, health, and energy. Once we get rid of it, then we can regain all of these back. If we are able to regain our energy, then we can easily adapt an active lifestyle.

Additionally, the author adds that this constant worrying over our weight stems from the fact that the smoking made us insecure. As soon as we get rid of the nicotine monster, then that insecurity will go away. In exchange, we get our confidence and self-respect back.

In succeeding chapter, the author will introduce us to the Easy Way to Stop Smoking. If we carefully follow the instructions, then he can guarantee that weight gain is nothing to worry about.

Avoid False Incentives

Some smokers try to use the Willpower Method coupled with false incentives to try to get them out of this horrible habit. But more often than not, this usually fails.

For example, someone would claim to stop buying cigarettes and save the money he so that he could buy himself a new gadget, or go on vacation with his family. The author explains that this usually fails because the incentive is false. The smoker doesn't really feel the pressure to quit smoking with that incentive. And since there is no real pressure to stop, he wouldn't feel bad about breaking the promise. Soon enough, he's back to smoking packs of cigarette a day.

Thus, if we want to stop smoking, we must really want to do it. There is no need for incentives and bribes. The mere fact that smoking offers nothing should be enough to make us quit.

The Easy Way to Stop

By now, we're finally ready for the Easy Way to stop smoking. According to the author, there are only two things we have to do. First, we must finally make the decision to quit; and second, we must not sulk about it. Instead, we should rejoice that we can finally be free from nicotine.

To prepare ourselves for the first step, the author wants to keep these pointers in mind:

- You are capable of achieving it. The only person in control of your own acts and thoughts is yourself. Thus, realize that the only person who can make you light another cigarette – or stop doing so – is yourself.

- There is nothing to lose. When we give up smoothing, we're not giving up anything we love. In return, we end up gaining so much.

- There is no such thing as one cigarette. The author explains that smoking is an addiction to a certain drug – nicotine – and one cigarette can cause another chain reaction.

- Smoking is a drug addiction, and not a sociable habit. Face the fact that you are addicted, and that the longer you run away from the cure, the worse you would become. Choose to face the cure today.

- Remember that the first moment you choose to stop smoking, you are already a non-smoker. Dwell on the fact that you are no longer a smoker, and rejoice in it. This will help you appreciate and enjoy life a whole lot more.

Once you have finally set your mind to finally quit smoking, there is a tendency to feel gloomy. This is all part of the process. The author explains that this unhappiness stems from the following:

- You have not fully embraced the abovementioned pointers. Give yourself time to believe and embrace each of the statements above.

- You fear failure. Remind yourself that you will succeed, and that any confidence trick wouldn't work on you because you are an intelligent person.

- You feel miserable about quitting, even if you believe all of the abovementioned pointers. Think about quitting as finally escaping prison – it is something to be happy about. Focus on that feeling of triumph.

Through these tips, the author guarantees that we would be able to develop the frame of mind necessary for the first step. Once we have finally decided to stop smoking, all that's necessary is to maintain that frame of mind throughout the withdrawal period. More on this will be discussed in the next chapter

But, before ending this chapter, the author issues the following warnings:

- As much as possible, he advises us to plan to fully put an end to smoking after finishing this book.

- The withdrawal period can last about three weeks. Make sure that your frame of mind is set to, "It's marvelous that I am never going to smoke again!" instead of, "I can survive three weeks without smoking". These statements can make a big difference.

The Withdrawal Period

Within three weeks after deciding to have a final cigarette, we should expect to experience withdrawal symptoms. According to the author, this may not only be caused by the withdrawal from nicotine, but may also be due to other psychological triggers from the stressors around us.

Again, the author reminds us that there is no physical pain during this period. If you think you're under physical pain, think again – it's highly likely that it's all in your head. The author shares that some smokers claim to experience hunger or stomach rumblings during this period. More often than not, it's the little nicotine monster that's actually hungry, not you.

To the heaviest smokers, this may be his most miserable period. When you experience this, keep on reminding yourself that there is nothing to be sad about. After all, you're not giving up anything. This decision will benefit you in so many ways, so why are you still moping about it? It is also necessary to remind ourselves that this feeling of unhappiness, if not countered at the onset, will only trigger the brainwashing process to start all over again.

During this period, it is necessary to keep on reminding yourself that cigarettes do nothing to help you. It is merely a prop. It cannot make occasions more sociable, neither does it complete a meal. It is not pleasurable at all. In fact, the only reason you crave it is due to a drug, nicotine. Make sure to reflect on these facts so that they can be gelled into your head eventually.

Nonetheless, the author doesn't want us to completely forget

135

about smoking. This exercise isn't about forgetting how to smoke at all. Instead, it is all about embracing the joys of never having to smoke again. After months or years of being chained to nicotine, you are finally free from it!

And finally, regardless of what you experience during this period, the most important thing is to never doubt your decision. As soon as you let an inkling of doubt cloud your thoughts, it will start a chain of negative emotions, which will ultimately defeat the purpose. As much as possible, focus on the wonderful reasons why you should stop smoking. Rejoice over the fact that you are no longer a prisoner to the nicotine monster. Most importantly, remember that this period is only temporary. Soon enough, you will just come to realize that you are no longer craving a smoke.

Just One Puff

During the withdrawal period, we may be tempted to take one or two puffs off of a cigarette. Sure, that first puff won't taste good anymore, so we may think that we're finally losing interest. However, the author shares that the opposite is true.

He reminds us that since we've been starving the nicotine monster for days or weeks already, just one puff would be enough to make it strong again – and send you flying back to square one. We all began with one puff, after all.

To keep our minds off of taking another puff, the author reminds us that doing so has two damaging effects. The first is that it keeps the monster alive, and the second is that it helps the monster convince us to take more puffs.

Thus, we shouldn't fall for the temptation of just one puff. Redirect your attention to the joys of being nicotine-free.

Will It Be Harder for Me?

The author notes that there will be times when we might think that the withdrawal period is harder on us than on others. After all, each of us have different circumstances, professions, and interests. We may think that some of us may have it easier because they're not under constantly high levels of stress on a daily basis.

More particularly, the author is sure that smokers from the medical profession would find the withdrawal difficult hard because of the following reasons:

- Their awareness of health risks creates fear.

- Their work is highly stressful.

- They feel guilty because they should be setting an example to others.

All these factors amplify his feeling of being deprived of what his body thinks is an escape from all his problems.

According to the author, these are all reminders from the nicotine monster that we have already stopped smoking. Instead of worrying and amplifying the negative emotions, we should rejoice that we are no longer under its control. It may seem hard, but the key is to develop a frame of mind that will unceasingly remind us to rejoice. Thus, regardless of age, profession, sex, or intelligence, as long as we have already developed that frame of mind, the author guarantees that we will find this process relatively easy.

The Main Reasons for Failure

According to the author, there are only two reasons to fail in this method: the influence of others, and having a bad day.

The first reason usually occurs during occasions and gatherings, where a companion would light up a cigarette. This situation can be especially tempting during our weakest moments. However, this wouldn't be a problem if we have already developed the rejoicing mindset. Thus, instead of sulking or feeling deprived, focus on the fact that you are no longer a prisoner of the nicotine monster. Besides, maybe you can inspire your friend to do the same.

The second reason for failure is having bad days, and thinking that smoking can make it better. However, we now know that smoking doesn't really help us relax – in fact, it can even make us more restless than we already are. When this happens to us, the author wants us to remember that everyone has bad days, whether he's a smoker or not, but non-smokers tend to cope with bad days better. The author goes on to explain that smoking will only cause us to feed the nicotine monster, without solving any of the real reasons why we're having a bad day.

Thus, we can easily triumph over these reasons for failure if we always keep a positive mindset.

Substitutes

At this point, the author wants to warn us against substitutes like chewing gum, herbal cigarettes, and pills. These substitutes are often encouraged an anti-smoking method, and are sometimes recommended by therapists and doctors. However, they do not solve the smoking problem; instead, they can make our situation worse.

For this chapter, the author wants us to remember these key points:

1. Nicotine has no substitute;

2. Nicotine is poison, so we don't need it in our body;

3. Cigarettes create voids instead of filling them.

From these pointers, it is clear that we must avoid substitutes which also contain nicotine, like gum, nasal spray, and patches. These substitutes contain the same amount of nicotine, which only add fuel to the addiction. After all, we cannot solve a drug problem by taking in the same drug – or any drug, for that matter.

During these times, we must remember that the real problem is the brainwashing. We're not really experiencing physical withdrawal pains – this illusion is simply created by the nicotine monster so that we may be lured into feeding it.

Thus, think of your withdrawal symptoms as your body's way of telling you that it is finally getting rid of all the nicotine in your system. Instead of moping about it, enjoy the fact that you are on your way to freedom and being poison-free.

Should I Avoid Temptation Situations?

To answer this question, the author wants to be more specific with his suggestion. He begins this chapter by explaining that the fear which keeps us smoking has two distinct phases.

The first phase consists of panic. This usually happens when a person who is dependent on nicotine realizes that he is running out of cigarette, but there are no stores anywhere in sight. According to the author, this panic isn't caused by withdrawal pangs; instead, it is due to a psychological fear of dependency. And fortunately, the fact that it is psychological should make you less worried about your situation. Trust this method and you will soon break free of this fear.

On the other hand, the second phase involves the fear of an unenjoyable future. To some smokers, they think that living without cigarette is a miserable life. They fear that they can no longer cope with trauma, or that they could no longer relax. However, this is all just part of nicotine's brainwashing. Once they are free, they will soon realize that the opposite is true.

Now that we have identified the two phases of fear, the author wants to discuss the two main categories of temptation avoidance.

- Some smokers avoid smoking, but keep a stash of cigarette within their reach because they claim to gain a confidence boost by simply knowing that they're there. Unfortunately, this method guarantees a higher rate of failure, compared to those who commit to completely discarding their cigarettes.

The author explains that the essential requirements in order to succeed with his method are certainty and a positive mindset. Having a positive mindset will not be enough, especially if the person is not committed to his goal.

- The second category of temptation avoidance includes situations. According to the author, it would be best for us to avoid stressful situations, but go out and enjoy social events. He goes on to add that putting ourselves in stressful situations wouldn't solve anything while, on the other hand, attending social events will help us enjoy the occasion. This will make us realize that we do not need nicotine in order to enjoy a party. And while you're at it, make sure to rejoice over the fact that you are another step closer to your goal.

The Moment of Revelation

About three weeks after a smoker puts out his final cigarette, he will be able to experience his moment of revelation. According to the author, this moment is the most beautiful part, since you no longer have to remind yourself that there is no need to smoke. And the best part about this moment is that it has a lasting effect, which guarantees that we would no longer be tempted to light another stick of cigarette.

But this doesn't mean that all of us would take three weeks to experience this moment. Depending on how committed a person is, he can either expect it to happen immediately or within a few months.

However, the author also wants to make it clear that the moment of revelation isn't something you patiently wait for day in and day out. Instead of just waiting for this magical moment, go out and enjoy everything that life has to offer. Don't sit around and worry that your moment of revelation hasn't arrived yet. Relax. Have fun. One day, you'll just wake up and realize that you've finally broken the chain.

The Final Cigarette

In a previous chapter, the author asks us to delay smoking until the end of this book. With everything discussed up until now, he acknowledges that we are now ready to smoke that final cigarette.

But before doing so, he wants us to make sure of the following:

- That we are certain and determined to reach our goal.

- That we are experiencing a sense of excitement over the fact that we are finally going to be free from the bonds of nicotine slavery.

Don't hesitate to take your time and assess your current situation. If you have doubts, then you're free to re-read this entire book. After all, you must be absolutely certain that you are ready to quit smoking, otherwise you'll keep falling back into the trap.

On the other hand, if you're already certain of success, the author simply wants us to follow these instructions:

1. Make a vow to completely give up smoking, and take that vow to heart.

2. As you smoke that last cigarette, do so consciously. Let the filth from the smoke fill your lungs with every puff you take, and ask yourself whether this is

something you really find pleasurable.

3. When you finally extinguish that last cigarette, embrace the feeling of freedom. Focus on how great it feels to be free from your nicotine slavery.

4. For around three weeks, you will experience cravings. This is a sign that the nicotine is finally exiting your body, so the nicotine monster is trying to lure you into taking another cigarette. During these times, the author wants us to focus on rejoicing that we are finally going to succeed in our mission to be a non-smoker.

5. And finally, we must continuously remind ourselves that we made the right decision. Doubting our decision to quit will only make us feel miserable, and as a result, would tempt us into lighting another cigarette.

If we carefully follow the abovecited instructions, then the author guarantees that we can finally say goodbye to smoking. To conclude this chapter, the author also wants to share the following tips:

•   It's worth reiterating that we should never doubt our decision.

•   Don't wait to become a non-smoker; instead, choose

to be one now.

- The moment of revelation will just happen. Don't waste your life away by waiting for that moment.

- Avoid using substitutes at all costs.

- When you see smokers, pity them because they are slaves to nicotine.

- Bad days happen to everyone – and a quick smoking break doesn't make a bad day become better.

- Whenever you feel the urge to smoke, remind yourself to rejoice over the fact that you are already a non-smoker today.

A Final Warning

Now that we're finally nicotine-free, we now have a fresh perspective on smoking. However, we shouldn't stop here.

According to the author, no matter how sure we are that we won't fall into the trap again, we must make a commitment to never smoke another cigarette. After all, our addiction began with only one cigarette.

To warn us against falling into the nicotine trap again, the author wants us to remember these simple reminders:

- Cigarette does nothing for us. Not only is it bad for our health, but it also promotes an antisocial behavior.

- Try to think of the horrible experience you had during the withdrawal period. Do you really want to experience the suffering all over again?

Feedback

The author has been advocating the Easy Way to stop smoking for over twenty years now. During this time, he has gathered enough information as to why it works and why others still have a hard time with this method.

To guarantee success with this method, the author was able to come up with a checklist to make the process easier for us. The checklist is as follows:

1. We should make a vow to never intoxicate yourself with nicotine – whether it be smoking, chewing, or sucking. But more importantly, we should stick to this vow and take it to heart.

2. Keep on reminding yourself that you're not giving up anything. Smoking offers no disadvantages, and neither does it provide us with genuine pleasure. It is merely a prop which we can get rid of whenever we choose to.

3. There is no such thing as a smoker who can't quit. All smokers fell for the same trap, and all of them can escape it.

4. If you're having doubts about your decision to quit, remind yourself of the cons of smoking vis-à-vis its pros, if any. This will make you realize that you made the right decision, since there really is nothing to gain

from smoking.

5. Don't avoid the thought of smoking. If it crosses your mind form time to time, rejoice over the fact that you are no longer a smoker.

6. Do not:

    a. Resort to using nicotine substitutes like gums or nasal sprays.

    b. Hesitate on throwing away all your packs of cigarettes.

    c. Avoid smokers.

    d. Drastically change your lifestyle just because you stopped smoking.

7. And finally, don't want for the moment of revelation to happen. Just go with how life flows, and one day you'll just realize that you're already free from the bonds of the nicotine monster.

Help the Smoker Left on the Sinking Ship

It is a known fact that all smokers, if given the chance to quit without being subjected to withdrawal pangs, would give up on smoking in an instant. Unfortunately, only those who are truly committed can make it through the process.

According to the author, the smokers who are left on the sinking ship are the ones who need help more than ever. When they see their friends finally giving up on smoking, they end up feeling hopeless – and as a result, they often turn to intoxicating themselves more with nicotine. More than ever, now is the time for ex-smokers to step up and help improve the lives of others.

Thus, those who successfully make it through the withdrawal stage have the duty to help other smokers get through this phase. Remind them that their fears are all psychological, and that withdrawal symptoms are all in their heads. But more importantly, we must remind them of the benefits of quitting, and how easy it is to break free.

After all, only a fellow smoker would know the struggle; and there could be no better source of inspiration than one who has successfully extinguished his last cigarette.

Advice to Non-smokers

As soon as you experience the moment of revelation, you would immediately want to tell the whole world about it – especially your friends who seem to have given up on quitting. However, the author advices that forcing a smoker to try the Easy Way isn't the best thing to do.

Instead, he advises us to surround the smoker with ex-smokers first. When he is constantly surrounded by people who successfully stopped smoking, the smoker can find inspiration and strength to do so himself. In contrast, if we try to force him to stop smoking immediately, he would end up feeling trapped, and that can only make his nicotine addiction worse. Allow him to open up to the idea of quitting in his own time.

Once he is finally ready to take the final cigarette, which would be the perfect time to make him read this book. He will find this new approach more refreshing – after all, other books filled with pictures and information on lung diseases couldn't possibly be inspiring.

During the withdrawal period, your friend will be overwhelmed by a variety of emotions. This can cause him to be irritable at times. When this happens, the author wants us to be more understanding about his situation. Instead, we should shower them with praises about their progress. And soon enough, they too will experience the moment of revelation.

Conclusion

Smokers all over the world can agree that quitting is never easy. Despite the various methods claiming to help smokers change their ways, none of them proved to be a hundred percent effective. That is – until Allen Carr's Easy Way came along.

In this books, Allen Carr details the method he used to overcome his chain-smoking habits. According to him, there are only two important steps: to commit and to keep a positive mindset.

To commit means to make a vow to finally put an end to smoking. But most importantly, we must promise to take that vow to heart. However, committing to this promise can take a toll on us, and that's when the second step comes along. This situation is particularly true during the withdrawal period.

According to the author, when we are tempted to light up a cigarette, we shouldn't allow ourselves to feel deprived. Instead, we should focus on the fact that we are only being tempted because we are no longer doing that nasty habit. We should focus on the fact that we have already decided to quit, and rejoice every moment that we remain free from nicotine slavery.

Nonetheless, maintaining this mindset doesn't mean that we always have to avoid social events. The author wants to make it clear that quitting doesn't involve a drastic change in the way we live. Instead of avoiding social events, he wants us to enjoy them. This will help us realize that we don't need cigarettes in order to be confident and sociable. And when we hear the nicotine monster asking for just one puff, rejoice over the fact that you are now in control of your life, and are no longer giving in to the requests of the monster.

Aside from social events, there are also other instances when our rejoicing mindset would be tested. These can include hanging out with fellow smokers, or simply watching a TV show where a character coolly lights a cigarette. Again, we must focus on the fact that we are no longer chained to the little monster in our head. We must always remind ourselves that we are only experiencing these temptations because the monster is starving, and is desperate for a taste.

Fortunately, studies reveal that it only takes around three weeks for our body to get rid of all the nicotine. This means that, on average, the withdrawal period only lasts for three weeks.

Soon enough, we will finally be able to experience the moment of revelation. The author describes this as the liberating feeling of knowing that we are no longer under the control of the little monster. He wants us to remember, however, that this feeling is not something that we have to wait for. Instead, it is something that just happens when we least expect it to happen.

To conclude, as long as we know how to follow a clear set of instructions, then we are already bound to succeed with the Easy Way. With nothing to give up and everything to gain, there is no reason for us to keep on delaying our plan to finally stop smoking.

Final Thoughts

Hey! Did you enjoy this book? We sincerely hope you thoroughly enjoyed this short read and have gotten immensely valuable insights that will help you in any areas of your life.

Would it be too greedy if we ask for a review from you?

It takes 1 minute to leave 1 review to possibly influence 1 more person's decision to read just 1 book which may change their 1 life. Your 1 minute matters and we value it and thank you so much for giving us your 1 minute. If it sucks, just say it sucks. Period.

FREE BONUS

P.S. Is it okay if we overdeliver?

Here at Abbey Beathan Publishing, we believe in overdelivering way beyond our reader's expectations. Is it okay if we overdeliver?

Here's the deal, we're going to give you an extremely valuable cheatsheet of "Accelerated Learning". We've partnered up with Ikigai Publishing to present to you the exclusive bonus of "Accelerated Learning Cheatsheet"

What's the catch? We need to trust you... You see, we want to overdeliver and in order for us to do that, we've to trust our reader to keep this bonus a secret to themselves. Why? Because we don't want people to be getting our exclusive accelerated learning cheatsheet without even buying our books itself. Unethical, right?

Ok. Are you ready?

Simply Visit this link: http://bit.ly/acceleratedcheatsheet

We hope you'll enjoy our free bonuses as much as we've enjoyed preparing it for you!

Free Bonus #2: Free Book Preview of Summary: Crushing It!

The Book at a Glance

Gary Vaynerchuk wrote Crushing It as a follow-up to his highly-acclaimed first book called Crush It. In the first book, he laid the foundation for the techniques and strategies that he used to build his own personal brand. He explained how he transformed a local liquor store into a multi-million dollar national operation. In this follow-up book, Vaynerchuk breaks down the strategies based on the most popular social networking platforms during the last few years namely Musical.ly, Snapchat, Twitter, YouTube, Facebook, Instagram, podcasts, and voice-first applications. Furthermore, for every chapter in the book, Vaynerchuk tells true stories of entrepreneurs who successfully implemented the principles he discussed in the first book.

Without further ado, here's a quick overview of the content that you should expect from this branding and business book:

Chapter 1: The reign of traditional marketing is over. Gone are the days wherein only the big corporations have the ability to reach out to legions of customers through marketing campaigns on television, radio, and newspapers. Even if you are just starting out as an entrepreneur, you have the same chances as the multi-national companies out there. If you can build an interesting personal brand, you can crush it in whatever business you want to enter.

Chapter 2: To build a profitable business around your personal brand, you need to focus on the things that really matter. In the words of Vaynerchuk, these are intent, authenticity, passion, patience, speed, work, and attention.

Chapter 3: Everything boils down to the quality of your content. If you offer unique content, people will follow you and pay attention to your every move. If you are offering the same content as everybody else, then you are pushing yourself down.

Chapter 4: Don't let anything stop you from pursuing your passion and making a business out of it. You have to deal with what Vaynerchuk refers to as the three fears: fear of failure, fear of wasting time, and fear of seeming vain.

Chapter 5: Vaynerchuk offers Pat Flynn as the perfect example of a guy who pursued his passion like crazy and emerged a very successful and rich man. Flynn is the man behind the very popular blog called Smart Passive Income. Flynn uses the blog to talk about the various successful online businesses he had built during the years.

Chapter 6: According to Vaynerchuk, the first thing you should do in building your personal brand is to create a Facebook page. Chances are most of your potential audiences are in Facebook. This alone should convince you to start being active on Facebook.

Chapter 7: To be discovered online, you have to be a dogged self-promoter. No one is going to promote yourself so you should might as well do it. This is especially true if you are just starting out. As your brand gets bigger, your followers will start promoting you. But this doesn't mean you should stop putting your name out there.

Chapter 8 to 15: Vaynerchuk goes in-depth in explaining the strategies you should follow in using the largest social media platforms out there namely Musical.ly, Snapchat, Twitter, YouTube, Facebook, Instagram, Podcasting, and voice-first technologies. If you really want to take your personal brand and business to the next level, these are the platforms you should be spending your time and resources on.

Introduction

We are now in a world where an eight-year-old kid and his dad can make thousands of dollars a week just by opening boxes of toys on YouTube. According to Vaynerchuk, this is the kind of world we live in right now. If you have the passion and the hustle for something, you can achieve almost anything you want. Vaynerchuk was lucky enough to have seen the trend during its early days and capitalized on it at full speed. He grew his family's $4 million liquor store into a $60 million business within the span of just a few years. How did he do it? He used as leverage all the tools and resources that the internet and technology have to offer. He created a personal brand and used it to grow his core business.

Now, Vaynerchuk divides his time between his wine business, his digital media company, and several other business projects. His operations now have offices in several cities including Los Angeles, New York City, Chattanooga, and London. He still takes the time to connect and engage with his followers on various social media sites like Twitter, Instagram, Facebook, and Snapchat. He's as busy as ever. He runs a YouTube show where he answers questions from fans. He maintains a daily video documentary. He plays a role in a television reality show called Planet of the Apps. And he's writing books in between.

Since his first book, Crush It, a lot has changed. This is why Vaynerchuk wrote a second book to expand on the topics he has discussed in the first book. He wants to update his readers about the latest information and developments on how to leverage internet platforms to create a lasting and powerful personal brand. The main difference between the first book and this one is that this one includes voices from other entrepreneurs who have achieved the same level of success as Vaynerchuk. These are entrepreneurs who achieved success by implementing the principles and concepts discussed in the first book.

A lot of entrepreneurs became successful after following the advice on Crush It. There's John Lee Dumas who started his own business podcast which now generates $200,000 a month. There's Louie Blaka who went from obscure art teacher to a thriving artist who now sells his paintings with price tags reaching up to five figures. He also hosts painting events that can attract a hundred people per event. These two successful entrepreneurs are just a few of the hundreds of people who achieved their goals after reading Crush It.

Chapter 1: The Path Is All Yours

Influencer marketing is quickly taking over traditional marketing. There's a reason why more and more companies are targeting online audiences instead of pumping money into television and print advertisements. Traditional marketing is on a downturn while online marketing continues to evolve as a powerful platform. Just think about it. More than a billion cumulative hours are spent every day on YouTube by its users. The average person spends at least one hour on Facebook every day. Around 4,000 videos and photos are posted on Instagram every hour. Needless to say, there's a changing of the guard here. In with the new and out with the old.

Since 2009, big brands have tripled the amount of money they spend on advertising that targets online audiences. Billions of dollars are being pumped into online platforms like social networking sites, blogs, forums, and applications. This is where you can get in with your own personal brand and get a piece of the pie. Being an influences in any niche can be very lucrative. There are brands out there who are more than willing to pay you top dollar just by posting a photo on Twitter or Facebook or Instagram. How legitimate is influencer marketing, you may ask. Well, it's legitimate enough that in 2016 alone, the top personalities on YouTube got paid $70 million.

Building yourself to be an influencer takes time. The steps you need to take to get to that point was discussed in detail by Vaynerchuk in his first book, Crush It. In the simplest of terms, an influencer is someone who builds an online audience which is big enough that brands are willing to pay him money if he posts a link, a story, a video, or a photo about their products and services. Have you ever come across a YouTube video wherein the person talks about a product or a service right after his core content? That's the most basic example of an online personality being paid to mention a brand's product or service. This is often referred to in the marketing industry as product placement. A lot of YouTubers make most of their money through these product placements.

Personal Brands Are For Everyone

Many people have the wrong assumption that personal brands are only applicable for creative types of people like artists, photographers, and musicians. It's true that a lot of those who were able to successfully monetize their personal brands are composed by these creative types. But that doesn't mean they are the only ones who can do it. Again, if you are passionate about something and you are willing to toil to create your personal brand, you can easily achieve what they have achieved. It doesn't matter where your passion lies. It can be about beekeeping or mountain climbing or stamp collecting. If you are good at it and you are passionate about it, there's absolutely no reason why you can't monetize it.

How I'm Crushing It: Amy Schmittauer, Savvy Sexy Social

Amy's rise as an online celebrity came as an accident. A video she made for a friend's wedding ceremony made her realize that she can tell stories that resonate with a lot of people. While working full-time at a law firm, Amy also worked part-time as a social media manager. She was contented with what she was making until she read Vaynerchuk's first book, Crush

It. She realized that she was worth much more so she quit her job and focused on building her own personal brand. Her earnings and reputation quickly grew. She now runs a video channel with nearly 100,000 subscribers. She has written best-selling books, created influential vlogging tutorial series, and presented as a keynote speaker in stages all over the world.

CPSIA information can be obtained
at www.ICGtesting.com
Printed in the USA
BVHW041427030919
557429BV00010B/359/P